TALES FROM WITNEY SCROTUM

Peter Tinniswood was born in Liverpool, and started his writing career when he joined *The Star* in Sheffield in 1958. Nowadays he devotes his time to writing novels, books, television and stage dramas and situation comedy. His 'Brandon' novels have been much acclaimed and his TALES FROM A LONG ROOM, featuring the Brigadier, were instant bestsellers. His BBC Television series 'I Didn't Know You Cared' is generally regarded as one of television's comedy classics.

TALES FROM WITNEY SCROTUM

Peter Tinniswood

Illustrated by
John Lawrence

ARROW BOOKS

Arrow Books Limited
62–65 Chandos Place, London WC2N 4NW

An imprint of Century Hutchinson Limited

London Melbourne Sydney Auckland
Johannesburg and agencies throughout
the world

First published in Great Britain by Pavilion Books Limited 1987

Arrow edition 1988

© Peter Tinniswood 1987
Illustrations © John Lawrence 1987

Phototypeset by Input Typesetting Limited, London
Printed and bound in Great Britain by
Anchor Brendon Limited, Tiptree, Essex

ISBN 0 09 957440 3

Contents

The Dedication

IT SEEMS to me that, if you take the trouble to write a book with all the inconvenience to your social life that entails, you might as well take equal trouble in dedicating it to the people you admire and the people you love.

So here goes.

This book is dedicated to:

Daniel Tinniswood.

Hazel and Sydney Tinniswood.

Wilfred Tinniswood.

Alfa Tinniswood and every other Tinniswood, particularly those in the beautiful county of Cumberland.

Alan Barrett, erstwhile professional of Castleton Moor Cricket Club.

Hugh Stirk and Rod Ritchings of Ashton-on-Mersey Cricket Club.

The former Miss Pat Lloyd of Carrington Lane.

My late friends Mr John Comer and Mr Fred Billany, whom I loved dearly.

Mr Tony Carter, journalist and fellow Lancastrian.

Mr Clive Morris of Cardiff.

Miss Pat Roberts and Mr Leslie Nutbrown of Sheffield.

Miss Liz Smith, Miss Shirley Dixon, Messrs Maurice Denham, Kenneth Cranston, Wilfred Wooller, Peter and Diana Skellern. (She's not a messr, but she knows what I mean.)

Albert Modley, Al Read and Dame Irene Thomas of *Round Britain Quiz*.

Mr Mike Bradwell, if he's sober.

The late Len Doherty, writer of genius.

Messrs Colin Backhouse of Sale, John Ikin of Lancashire and Staffordshire, Richard Hutton of Yorkshire and England, and his dad, Mr Cyril Sidlow of Liverpool FC and his colleague the great Mr Billy Liddell.

Mesdames Margaret Mattheson, Judy Lowe, Vanda Godsell and the nice lady from the freezer shop with the hazel eyes.

The late Mr Winston Place of Lancashire and England.

Ex King Constantine of the Hellenes – nice cove, don't you think?

The ticket collector at Hampton Court station and Mr Samuel Beckett.

The sublime Miss Carole Thatcher and the equally sublime Mr Ned Sherrin of Rochdale Hornets Rugby League Football Club.

Mr Tom Gillhespy of Cardiff.

Miss Philippa D'Eath of the same city.

Sir Gordon Linacre.

I don't know any other 'sirs', but they're all welcome on my list.

Mr Frank Johnson, ex Sale County Grammar School for Boys.

Mr Sid Clegg of Idle, Bradford.

The milkman and the dustman, in the hope that he might leave us a few more black plastic bags each week.

Sir Jack Hobbs, Cyril Washbrook, Alan Wharton, Ken Grieves, Eric and Geoffrey Edrich, Peter Greenwood, Malcolm Hilton and Tommy Greenhough.

The great and sublime and incomparable Mr J.B. Statham of Lancashire and England.

Our local Volvo dealers.

The utterly delectable Miss Carla Lane.

The equally delectable Mr Jim Lowental who comes in to fix the pilot light on our central heating boiler.

Mr Stephen Wood of the National Theatre, in the hope that he'll stop ringing up pretending he's Sir Geoffrey Boycott.

The delectable Miss Sue McGregor and the equally delectable Mr Allen Kassell.

Alan E. Howard and those ghastly buggers from the Inland Revenue who keep pestering me.

Oh yes, and all the boys and girls from the VAT offices at Southend.

The cast of *EastEnders* – isn't Dirty Den the spitting image of Norman Tebbit? Well, I think so, anyway.

Denise and John from over the road.

Mr Peter Harvey, Mr Stuart Machin and Miss Peggy Crowther of Sheffield.

Mr Noel Upfold.

Upfold – isn't that a lovely name?

I must use it in one of my books later, if I can find the time to write one.

The distinguished cellist, Mr Julian Lloyd-Webster.

Mr Denis Compton, Mr John Price, Mr Laurie Fishlock, Mr Bill Bowes and Mr Alec Bedser.

Mr Ralph Hawkins who hasn't written to me for ages. Get in touch, you bastard!

All the night shift at the ointment warehouse.

Mr Joe Ashton MP.

Mr Joe Leonard and Mr Derek Thomas and Mr Ken Shergold of Quidhampton in the lovely county of Wiltshire. And their wives, of course.

Finally, this book is dedicated to all those I have forgotten to mention.

The Introduction

THE BRIGADIER sent for me.

He was tired.

He had had a distressing row with his lady wife over the 'vexed question' of the provision of unlimited free bus passes for Mr Raymond Illingworth.

He had run out of green blotting paper.

But he was excited.

And for good reason.

It was, he told me, the greatest year in the whole glorious history of cricket.

'Imagine the splendour of it, Vileness,' he said. 'Two hundred years of playing our beloved "summer game" at headquarters.

'Send up the lifeboat maroons, light bonfires on our highest Northern Fells, sprinkle itching powder into Dame Peter West's best dancing pumps, creep up softly behind the Archbishop of Canterbury and shout "pillock" as loudly as you can into his right ear.

'Yes, my dear Tinniswood, you've guessed it – this year marks the bicentenary of Witney Scrotum Cricket Club.'

11

The Brigadier, it transpired, wanted me to chronicle the events of that memorable year.

'We'll publish a small private edition, Vileness,' said the Brigadier. 'I'm sure dear old Bruce Woodcock of *The Times* will lend you his John Bull printing set.'

Having a pedigree parrot, a pedigree poodle and a wife to support, I readily agreed.

This is what happened . . .

1
Hitting The Truth

I ARRIVED in Witney Scrotum on a knee-chapped afternoon in late January.

The Brigadier and his lady wife met me off the high speed moving train at Graveney Junction.

'Whatho, Vileness,' said the Brigadier, vigorously yanking the fingers of his left glove from the tray of the Nestle's chocolate bar dispenser.

He tipped the engine driver generously, and I noted that the porter who removed my baggage from the outside roof rack was wearing coral pink lipstick and pale mauve eyeshadow.

'What a character, eh?' said the Brigadier, affectionately belabouring him about the shoulders with the sharp end of his stumper's mallet. 'Must be well into his eighties and still knows how to dance backwards. Spitting image of Princess Michael of

13

the Huns, don't you think? Or am I thinking of Patsy Hendren?'

The lady wife snorted and conducted us imperiously to the trusty Lanchester waiting impatiently in the station yard, and after removing the cap from her bottle of vintage Airwick, placing it in the breast pocket of my thermal blazer and shaking me violently by the ears, instructed me to sit in the back seat next to her Bedlington terriers.

They drew back their lips and growled, exposing shrivelled gums and wizened, yellowing teeth.

'Silence, you brutes,' thundered the Brigadier. 'Silence.'

He commenced to attempt to fasten himself into his seat belt, trapping the fingers of his right glove in the buckles and nearly garrotting himself as the end of his muffler coiled itself fiercely round a stanchion.

As I watched his struggles I was reminded most forcibly of the sight of that sweet little Matthew Engels of *The Manchester Guardian* trying vainly to strap himself to the space bar of his typewriter in the front row of the press box at Buxton.

Presently, the Brigadier successfully concluded his exertions with a bay of triumph, and with a gludder and a gollop and a shower of sparks we set off for Witney Scrotum.

Dusk was falling as we lurched and groaned round the gentle, rolling country lanes of the rural West Country.

The headlamps of the trusty Lanchester picked out the startled eyes of badger and hare and Minor Counties umpires up to no good.

The waters of that most glorious of all English

chalk streams, the Somerset Kitchen, rilled and crooned in the moonlight. The woodlands of hanging oak, beech and chestnut hunched themselves into the brooding flanks of the Mendis Hills.

'Have you made a rude noise in the back seat there?' said the lady wife.

'No,' I said.

Nonetheless, she turned in her seat, yanked up the wick of the bottle protruding from the pocket of my blazer and ground her teeth most fearsomely.

The Bedlington terriers growled in sympathy.

'Brutes,' bellowed the Brigadier. 'Utter brutes.'

And he ground the gears of the car most generously.

We passed through the villages of Milton Abbas and Milton Arthur. We wheezed our way slowly up the steep incline out of Crowe Magna and at the summit paused to give a moment's respite to the panting Lanchester.

And there below us slumbering peacefully in the damp tuck of the valley lay the village of Witney Scrotum.

I could dimly make out the lights of the Golf Ball Museum and the glow from the eternal bonfire in old Grannie Swanton's garden as she burned yet another remaindered copy of Miss Jilly Cooper's *The Book of the Green Wellie*.

The Brigadier handed me his hip flask filled to the brim with home-made gin distilled, as he told me later, from a pair of redundant binoculars, and presently we commenced the descent into the village.

We crossed the river at the old stone packhorse bridge at Dredge's Elbow and with seven shuddering U-turns and a resounding clatter and scrunching of mudguards finally negotiated the gentle corner at the ancient artesian Popplewells.

How familiar the scene.

How the heart soared and fluttered as we entered the outskirts of Witney Scrotum.

Nothing had changed.

Oil lamps burned faintly in the windows of the cottages of the long-defunct gimlett and tremlett makers, who once long ago in the days of their prime had supplied the implements for toad circumcisers the length and breadth of the nation.

We passed the water meadows at Cowdrey's Bottom, skulking darkly in the deep black shadows cast by the massive buttresses of Botham's Gut.

The night shift at Fearnley's Mill was hard at work turning out yet another special consignment of thatched space invader machines for the Belgian royal family.

The village idiot, old Ben Stansgate, was relieving himself contentedly in the Ned Sherrin memorial horse and cattle drinking trough outside the Baxter Arms.

Old Squire Brearley sat high astride the wrought iron gates outside his exquisite Queen Anne mansion baying at the moon, and outside the Cricket Bag Repository Prodger the poacher waved gaily at us and exposed himself.

I thought to myself, could there possibly be a spot on earth more blessed and endowed with such beauty and tranquillity?

I was contemplating sending these thoughts in a billet-doux to Mr Christopher Martin-Jenkins, when there appeared before us, pedalling furiously on her motorised tricycle, the familiar figure of Miss Roebuck of the dog biscuit shop.

She extended her arm stiffly to the left and then turned right.

The cow catcher on the front of the Lanchester clipped her rear offside wheel and catapulted her violently into the ditch where ran the untreated overflow from Farmer Emburey's scrumpy parlour.

'Typical bloody spinster,' growled the Brigadier as he accelerated away from the sodden form clawing its way desperately out of the steaming watercourse. 'They're always the same when they're suffering from the Benaudpause.'

We turned into the front drive of the Brigadier's residence, and the Bedlington terriers immediately leapt to their hind legs and began to howl and scratch at the windows.

'Down, you brutes. Down!' shouted the Brigadier, and he turned to me and said: 'They always do this, when they see home. I would, too, but I'm driving.'

We disgorged ourselves from the car, and the Brigadier showed me to my quarters.

It was the usual place – an attic room, uncarpeted, unheated, sparsely furnished, littered with owl droppings and with a simple frieze depicting scenes in the history of British Home Stores.

'I know you cricket writing wallahs appreciate discomfort and deprivation. I've see you "at it" in Australia,' said the Brigadier as he thrashed the camp bed into shape with the end of his boot. 'We had dear old Bruce Woodcock of *The Times* here for ten days last year and he enjoyed every minute of it.

'Look over there and you'll see how he scribbled

on the wall with his Biro, marking the days off. He used to make tapping noises, too, on the hot water pipes. Can't think why.

He left me to my own devices for a while, and I took the opportunity of unpacking my seventeen pairs of Damart pyjamas, my Royal Swedish Air Force surplus flying jacket and my fur-lined Battle of Britain siren suit, which would, I knew, if worn in consort in bed give me some slight protection from the rigours of the night and the attentions of the Bedlington terriers.

I took out my pen and wrote on the wall, adding my name to the list of distinguished guests who had suffered nocturnal confinement in that pipe-clanking, starling-scuttering, bat-fluttering room beneath the eaves.

I examined the names.

There were the old familiars:

Robin Marlar (surely it was high time he learned how so spell his name properly?).

Neil Durden-Smith (and in my opinion the appended comment written in a different hand beneath his name was most definitely not called for).

John Kay, Bill Bowes, Denzil Batchelor, Maureen Lipman (who filled up one whole wall), and someone who omitted to write his christian name, contenting himself with the rather unusual surname, Help.

After a while the intense cold and the snoring of elderly owls forced me to descend the stairs and enter the Brigadier's study.

'Whatho, Vileness,' he said. 'Care for a snorter before supper?'

I nodded my head rapidly and gratefully, and he poured out two stiff measures of Whyte and Mackay blended Scotch whisky.

'Dear old Butch, dear old Slasher,' said the Brigadier, sipping contentedly from his tumbler. 'Thank God they had the infinite good sense to go into the distilling business after giving up cricket.

'I'm not so sure about Gertrude Bell, though.'

I looked around and marvelled how little the room had changed since my last visit on the occasion of the Witney Scrotum Cavalcade of Heavy Rollers and Exhibition of Bad Tempers Through the Ages.

The death mask of his father still stood on his desk, pipe reamer rammed into his right ear and Dunhill pipe cleaners protruding from the nostrils.

In the corner by the french windows stood a section of the sightscreen from Bramall Lane, still bearing the original tooth marks of Mr Brian Close.

And standing haughtily on top of the fretwork hat stand was the distinctive shape of the stuffed macaw, Dexter.

The Brigadier lit his bent-stem pipe and said:

'Well then, Vileness, what news of London? Still heaving with Arabs, is it?'

I nodded.

'Scum,' said the Brigadier. 'I am not a prejudiced man, but if I had my way, I'd . . .'

He was interrupted by the lady wife who entered the study bearing a tray on which were various items which seemed to be vaguely of an edible nature.

'Ah, fodder,' said the Brigadier. 'Goodo.'

As soon as the lady wife left the room he tipped

19

the contents of the tray into a large waste paper basket made from the dried skins of pre-war West Indian fast bowlers.

Then he continued:

'It's those bloody trams I can't stand in London. Great clanking things, belching out electricity all over the streets.

'And those frightful fogs – ghastly. I once got inextricably lost in the Café Royal for three days in one of those pea-soupers. I spent the time shadow-boxing with Bombardier Billy Wells.

'Last time I was there I'm pretty certain I saw Ronnie Corbett and his sister, Olga, the gymnast. I thought he was damnably good in *Steptoe and Son*. I liked the way he took his teeth out and wore those disgusting mittens all covered in gravy browning. Uncanny resemblance to Mr Barry Wood of Lancashire and Derbyshire, don't you think?'

He sighed and poured out two more measures of whisky. They were infinitely stiffer than the previous two.

'The first time I went to London was with my late lamented father of vile and loathsome memory,' he continued, slucking contentedly at his pipe. 'I was very young at the time. Even younger than Joe Hardstaff Junior. We went to my father's club, and I remember sitting outside eating quails' eggs and drinking mulled claret out of my school cap.

'Then we went to some rather fine house in Sussex Gardens where my father said he had some chairs to be re-caned.

'I remember sitting on the front doorstep eating oysters and caviare and drinking chilled hock from my father's masonic attaché case and wondering at the constant stream of male visitors who to my untutored eyes seemed unduly furtive in the pursuit of furniture restoration.

'And then this young lady came out. She smelled of patchouli and umpires' huts. If she hadn't been wearing a feather boa and black corsets, I would have sworn it was Sir Pelham "Mind My Bike" Warner. She looked me up and down, prodded my ribs with her toe and said: "Here's a penny from your pa. Go and buy yourself a platform ticket at Paddington station."

'And then, shortly after, father came out limping slightly and perspiring and we sat for five solid hours staring at Cleopatra's Needle.'

'Why?' I asked.

'Because it was his great ambition in life to be present when the bloody thing drooped and finally fell down,' he said, and then a broad and warm smile came to his face and he added: 'He died an unfulfilled man.'

The I Zingari wall clock struck nineteen minutes past eight, and the Brigadier poured out more whisky.

'You know why I've invited you here, Vileness?'

I nodded.

'This is the greatest year in the history of our beloved "summer game", and it is my intention that you record the events.'

I nodded again.

'I know what it's like with you writer chappies. You'll do anything for a free pint of ale and a mention on *Start the Week* with Dame Richard Baker.'

I was bound to concur, having once taken a net

21

under the most intimate of circumstances with Miss Claire Rayner.

'Well then,' said the Brigadier. 'Are you agreeable? If you do the job well, I might be able to wangle you a works visit to Chad.'

'It's a deal,' I said.

He scowled with pleasure.

'There's just one thing, though,' I said.

'Oh yes? And what is that?' he said. 'And before you answer would you be so kind as to remove the debris of your parrot's hindquarters from your beard?'

I did so and continued:

'Don't you think the book might clash with the bicentenary of Lord's?'

The words had a most remarkable and frightening effect upon him.

His cheeks turned puce.

His plus fours quivered.

His tie pin whirred anti-clockwise.

'Bicentenary of Lord's?' he roared. 'Balderdash, my dear sir. Absolute balderdash.'

I raised my eyebrows.

'And would you kindly not raise your eyebrows in that fashion,' he said. 'It shows up your bald patches.'

I looked suitably contrite.

The Brigadier took two long draughts from his tumbler of whisky, poured himself another and then said quietly and with considerable composure:

'Let me tell you something about Lord's and the MCC, Vileness.

'They are without exception a total shower of rampant charlatans.'

I thought of raising my eyebrows, but desisted
and said:

'Why?'

'Because, my dear bloodshot-eyed Emaciation,
they are nowhere near celebrating two hundred
years of unbroken cricket. It's all a cod. All this
palaver they're kicking up with requests on the
Jimmy Young Show on the talking wireless, adverts
in *Fur and Feathers*, and outings for senior citizens
on the Inland Waterways – it is done for one plain
and simple reason.

'They want to steal the thunder of the WSCC –
The Witney Scrotum Cricket Club.'

'Why?' I said once more.

Old journalistic habits die hard, as Mr Bernard
Levin will testify, if he can remember.

'Because they're a load of out-and-out stinkers,'
said the Brigadier. 'Let me put you and your fellow
inky scribes into the picture.'

He poured himself yet another glass of whisky
and slid the decanter to me across the coffee table
shaped in the form of the lower parts of Mr Mike
Gatting.

'As you well know, Vileness,' he said, 'the
precursors of the MCC were the White's Conduit
Cricket Club. Think about it, my dear sir. Think
about their initials – WCCC. Is that firmly fixed in
your mind? WCCC.'

I nodded.

The fumes of whisky were coiling themselves
behind my several eyeballs and making the strap of
my wristwatch twitch uncontrollably.

'Well then, sir, no one disputes the fact that in
1787 the WCCC turned themselves into the Maryle-

bone Cricket Club – the MCC. What is not known is that when they ordered their headed notepaper from W. H. Smith and his ghastly sons, the printer allowed the M in their initials to turn upside down and thus revert to W. The scum were so drunk that they didn't notice it. And so for forty-odd years all their correspondence and posters were adorned with the initials, WCC.

'The MCC, my dear Vileness, did not exist.'

'Gosh,' I said.

It seemed the most appropriate comment to pass – a pertinent point I learned to my cost on my wedding day many years previously.

The Brigadier purred with pleasure.

He tapped out his pipe on the end of his father's nose.

He eased a ruck in his underpants with the blunt end of his stumper's mallet.

He spoke again.

'All this bicentenary of the MCC is bunkum. It wasn't until Mr E. W. "Gloria" Swanton stumbled upon the mistake in 1827 that the matter was rectified. All those silly buggers sitting on the balcony of the Lord's Pavilion, smug and self-satisfied – their bloody club is still a babe in arms compared with us here in Witney Scrotum.'

I wanted to say Gosh once more, but an angry fleck of spittle appeared on the Brigadier's upper lip and a flush appeared on the front of his plus fours, so I desisted.

'I'll tell you another thing,' he said. 'You know all that rot about the turf of the original Lord's being transferred to the present ground?'

'Yes,' I said.

'Bilge, piffle and poppycock,' he said, his face growing more puce by the minute. 'Do you want to know what really happened?'

I tried to nod, but my chin seemed to be pinned to my chest as though it had been affixed to the latest volume of the essays of Mr Trevor Bailey.

The Brigadier chuckled.

'Let me tell you the truth about the matter,' he said. 'Conventional canon has it that the turf now gracing Lord's was removed from the old original ground at Dorset Square in 1811. All lies. What really happened is this: the workmen who removed the turf from Dorset Square repaired to a public hostelry in Islington for a pint or two and a game of Trivial Pursuit, leaving the turves outside on the pavement unattended.

'Now it so happened that a few lads from Witney Scrotum happened to be passing by in their empty waggon having previously delivered a consignment of cricket bag carcasses to Smithfields Market.

'They saw the turves lying in a great mound with no one to guard them and at once all their natural country instincts came flooding out – baseness, mendacity and rampant kleptomania.

'In an instant they jumped down, transferred the turves to their waggon and brought them back here to Witney Scrotum.'

'And so?' I said.

'And so, my dear Vileness, the cricket ground here at our beloved Witney Scrotum bears the original turves from Lord's. The other ground at headquarters is but a sham. You see, they couldn't admit to the public what had happened so they nipped across the river and stole the turves from The Oval.

'Well, The Oval couldn't admit the disgrace so they headed east and stole the turves from Chelmsford.

'Chelmsford then stole the turves from Sevenoaks, who journeyed north and raided Old Trafford, who instantly retaliated by crossing the Pennines and . . . nothing, my dear sir, you see is quite what it seems in this nauseous, revolting and disgusting world of ours.'

We finished our drinks and stepped outside the house.

Stars crackled in the frosty sky.

Drunken voices curdled the darkness from the snug bar of the Baxter Arms.

We passed by the parish church with its blessed statuettes of St Kevin de Keegan, the patron saint of endorsements and short hairy legs, and its relic of the saintly Tony Greig of the Sorrows, the money belt ripped from his person during the tragic Exodus from Sussex and England, and stepped on to the cricket ground.

All was silence.

All was bathed in moonlight.

'Lord's,' said the Brigadier, pointing at the square. 'The original Lord's, pristine and chaste as it was all those years and years ago.'

Tears came to our eyes.

We did the only thing two gentlemen of cricketing bent could possibly do.

With pleasure, relief and boundless humility we watered those blessed turves.

2
A Walk with Miss Roebuck

I AWOKE stiff with cold.

My limbs ached.

My eyeballs rattled in ice-encrusted sockets.

Frost crackled in my beard and in the folds of the aged army greatcoat scrunched up on top of me as I cowered in the mouse-squeaked darkness.

The camp bed wobbled and swayed.

During the night its motion had been so violent that I had been compelled to take three of the sea sickness pills I had brought with me for just such an eventuality.

I dressed myself hurriedly and hobbled down to breakfast.

'Whatho, Vileness,' said the Brigadier. 'Sleep well last night, did you?'

I clenched my teeth and nodded my head grimly.

'Good,' said the Brigadier. 'Sorry to tell you that the hot fodder's all gone. You'll have to make do with the cold fodder. Do you fancy a helping of congealed sago and custard?'

I declined the invitation and made do with a half-sucked Zube I had concealed in the ticket pocket of my thermal blazer for just such an emergency.

The Brigadier excused himself for the morning.

He was to visit his closest friend and next door neighbour, the Commodore, to discuss that worthy's recent and ruinously expensive purchase of the antique Zimmer used by Mr Raymond Illingworth in his last season as captain of the Leicestershire County Cricket Club.

I was about to search the baskets of the Bedlington terriers in pursuit of an odd bone or two to suck, when the lady wife threw open the door and said:

'You have a visitor. And would you please remove that gilbert dangling from your moustache.'

I did so immediately and into the room was ushered Miss Roebuck of the dog biscuit shop.

The lady wife glared at us.

'If you're thinking of hanky panky, I beg you to think of that fine old English precept which has kept this nation pure and great over the centuries of our stirring history – do it out of sight of the dogs.'

She slammed the door behind her.

Miss Roebuck blushed.

I am bound to confess that to this very day I am still not certain as to Miss Roebuck's comprehension of my true marital state.

I am a happily married man.

My wife is everything a man could desire in a consort – she is an avid member of the Folio Society and has been on many of their coach trips to the seaside, she knows how to work the new electric kettle and is a more than competent fielder in the leg trap.

Yet on this morning Miss Roebuck had obviously and patently made an effort.

She was dressed in a brand new pink angora twin-set and a kilt of the Black Watch tartan.

She wore a diamanté brooch in the shape of Mr Richie Benaud's mouth.

She had applied a brand new dressing of Polyfilla to the acne spots on her chin, her eyelids fluttered free and painted behind her rimless spectacles and she had doused herself liberally with after shave lotion.

'Shall we go for a walk?' she said. 'I've put my flatties on special.'

I nodded.

The great outdoors of a bleak English winter seemed at that moment eminently more preferable to the icy, gale-blasted wastelands of the interior of the Brigadier's home.

We stepped outside.

How beautiful the vista!

How magnificent!

Ravens wheeled and tumbled above the massive buttresses of Botham's Gut. The pantiles on the roof of the Golf Ball Museum glistened with thin-skeined rain. Old Grannie Swanton whirred merrily down the High Street on her roller skates hot foot for the season's first meet of The Shakin' Stevens Fan Club.

And in the front garden the snowman built by the Brigadier and the Commodore stooped and crumbled in the weak winter sunshine looking for all the world like Mr H.D. 'Dicky' Bird standing at Worksop as the shoulders sagged and melting snow dribbled down his chin.

'Has anyone ever told you you're the spitting image of Richard Hutton?' said Miss Roebuck with a blush.

I shook my head.

I didn't have the heart to tell her that I had once been mistaken for Mr Harry Pilling when I was five years of age.

'I once saw Richard Hutton at Taunton,' she said. 'He was buying a tea towel at Timothy White and Taylors. Isn't it nice the way county cricketers buy tea towels just like us?'

I nodded.

'I expect they get skin diseases like us, too,' she said.

We climbed over the crooked stile that led to the water meadows at Cowdrey's Bottom.

The rough pasture was hummocked with tangles of frost-blackened grass. A trio of mute swans wheezed low and slowly overhead. Prodger the poacher looked up from the hedge where he was emptying his traps, waved gaily and exposed himself.

'I don't know how he can do that in this weather, do you?' said Miss Roebuck.

We stumbled on over the uneven terrain.

My arch supports began to leak and my Thermogene spats began to curl and wrinkle.

Suddenly Miss Roebuck stopped dead in her tracks and grasped me urgently by the arm.

She began to pant.

Her temples twitched uncontrollably.

Her lips quivered and her eyes rolled.

'I've got to say it,' she said. 'I can't contain it any longer. I've just got to blurt it out.'

Good God, she's going to proposition me, I thought.

I looked round for ways of escape.

The river was flooded and the swollen flanks of the water swirled and swooshed deeply over the ford. I had taken the precaution of bringing my frogman's flippers with me from London, but like a damn fool I had left them back at the Brigadier's. The bull in the next field looked benign enough, but then so does Mr Robin Marlar and we all know what happens if you cross him.

I was trapped.

I began to perspire.

It wasn't that I didn't find Miss Roebuck attractive in an 'English rose' sort of way. Indeed, I have to confess that I found her innocence of the ways of the world curiously appealing. A young lady of her age, and she still believed that Mr Jack Simmons had been born under a gooseberry bush.

And yet what passions lurked behind that pale, earnest face? What emotions coursed through that frail, delicate body as she lay in bed at nights dreaming of dancing the tango with Mr Colin Dredge? What carnal desires swept through her mind as she applied sellotape to the covers of her old Rupert annuals?

And now?

Now she was dragging me down to sit beside her on an old tree stump. She was clawing at the zips on my flying jacket. She was . . .

'I've just got to tell you,' she said. 'I just can't keep it back any longer.'

'What?' I said hoarsely. 'For God's sake, what?'

'I think the plans for the bicentenary celebrations are absolutely awful,' she said.

'What?' I said. 'What?'

I found my shoulders heaving, my ankles throbbing and great waves of relief coursing through my veins, like the beer spewing down the throats of hairy-navelled Australians on the Saturday of the Lord's Test.

I felt an urgent desire to giggle.

Miss Roebuck took hold of my hand.

'There,' she said, lowering her head and blushing once more. 'I've said it. I've not told a soul in the world before. Not even Miss Denning, and I got very indiscreet with her last Wednesday night when we were discussing the relative merits of Graham Dilley and Sue Lawley.'

I said as gravely as I could:

'Come on. It's too cold to be sitting out in the open. Let's continue the walk, and you can tell me all about it.'

She needed no second bidding.

Soon we had crossed the river by the bridge next to the Temperance Hamster Farm and were striding out in the woods, and she was in full flood.

'Well, all they've decided to do basically is to hold a match on the day of the bicentenary with a team of celebrities. Honestly, I ask you. You know what'll happen there, don't you?'

'No,' I said.

'Well, they'll promise to bring Michael Parkinson and Joan Collins and Blake Carrington and Brian Redhead and Tim Brooke-Taylor and half the cast of *EastEnders* and on the day they'll turn up with ten homo dressers from the National Theatre and Peter Skellern.'

I was bound to agree that it was indeed a gloomy prospect, particularly if Mr Skellern insisted on playing the piano.

'And do you know what else they've arranged?' said Miss Roebuck, nimbly springing over the vast mounds of an abandoned badger sett.

'No,' I said.

'Well, the Commodore's putting on an exhibition of his cigarette cards and there's going to be a celebration dinner at the Baxter Arms and I just know the food will be horrid and the women will get drunk and there'll be fighting and swearing and the men will start singing rude songs and balancing pints of beer on their heads and I'll ladder my tights and my make-up will start to drip and I'll come out in worry spots on my elbows and shins and . . . and if only we had a hot-pot supper everyone would go down with food poisoning before there was time to get drunk.'

I was panting to keep up with her as we reached the crest of the valley's ridge and looked down into the next valley where the first trickle of the River Alley commenced its long and languid meander through the soft, smoking villages of Hammond Chase.

She stopped and turned to me, the wind whipping back her black chiffon scarf and whistling through her curlers.

'I'm right, aren't I?' she said fiercely. 'Aren't I? Aren't I?'

'I don't know,' I said. 'Have you got any plans of your own?'

'Have I got any plans of my own?' she said, her eyes beginning to sparkle and twinkle. 'I've got oodles of them. Oodles and oodles.'

A light, sleet-cold drizzle began to fall, and we were compelled to take shelter in the old piano tuners' emergency hut in the lee of the tor.

We settled ourselves on kapok-lined piano stools and I said:

'Go on then, Miss Roebuck. Tell me about your plans.'

'Well, I thought we should do a musical,' she said.

'A musical?'

'Yes,' she said. 'A musical about cricket.'

'What a good idea,' I said.

She smiled coyly.

'I knew you'd understand,' she said. 'Haven't you written books about cricket in the past yourself?'

'Vaguely,' I said. 'Only vaguely.'

She smiled again, but this time there was a glint of triumph in her eyes.

'Well, I've done something about it!' she said.

'What?'

'I wrote to that Andrew Lloyd-Webster, and I asked him if he'd like to do it. Well, he is quite well known, isn't he?'

I nodded.

'I told him I thought it was only right and proper to give work to people who come from our part of the world – look after our own boys, I say. And I said he could have full use of the village hall and all its facilities plus a share of the catering profits. And Prodger the poacher would provide accompaniment on his piano accordion if he should wish to provide us with nice music for a change. I even said he could bring his wife, if she promised not to sing.'

'And what happened?' I said.

'Well, he wrote back an awfully nice letter on real lined notepaper,' she said. 'And he said he'd have loved to do it and was very flattered, etc, etc, blah, blah, blah, but unfortunately he was already writing a musical with Clive Rice of Nottinghamshire and South Africa.'

'What a pity,' I said. 'Did he say what the musical was about?'

'Yes,' she said. 'The RAC Rally.'

The sleet stopped and the sun blasted its rays suddenly through the leaden sky for all the world like some gigantic MCC blazer that urgently needed a visit to the dry cleaners.

'Come on,' I said. 'Let's go and have some lunch.'

'Lovely,' she said. 'I love having lunch, specially if it's at midday.'

On the way down from the summit of the ridge she told me more of her plans.

She had had the idea of writing a pageant depicting some of the more heroic and exciting deeds in the life of Colin Dredge.

She was going to call it Dredge of Arabia or

Dredge of the Antarctic, and she had invited Donald Sinden to play the leading role.

'And what happened?' I asked as we passed through the rusting, creaking iron gate that led into Farmer Emburey's yard.

'Oh, he said he'd love to do it, if it didn't interfere with his elocution lessons,' she said. 'The trouble was Colin Dredge wasn't available to play the part of Amundsen's huskies. He said he didn't fancy having to have the Parvo injections.'

Having had some problems with actors and their unavailability in the past, I sympathised most heartily with her and confessed I still felt some bitterness at Miss Dorothy Tutin's late withdrawal from the part of Uncle Mort.

I helped her retrieve her left shoe which had somehow been slucked deep into a mound of gurgling, pulsating domestic refuse standing outside Farmer Emburey's front door.

'What he needs is a good woman to look after him,' said Miss Roebuck.

I nodded, but felt in my bones that he was more in need of a good left arm spinner to partner him in the multifarious vicissitudes of life.

We reached the metalled road that led to the village and struck out for the Baxter Arms.

Suddenly Miss Roebuck stopped me and whispered urgently:

'What do you think to what Somerset have done to Viv Richards and Joel Garner? Horrid, isn't it? It's quite disgusting. I know they're darkies, but that's no reason to treat them as such, is it?'

We stepped into the public bar of the Baxter Arms.

A Walk with Miss Roebuck

Miss Roebuck clung to me tightly and said:

'Fancy going into a pub at lunchtime. Denis Compton would do his nut if he could see us, wouldn't he?'

The bar was near deserted.

In a corner by the bleak-eyed fire sat Don 'Sir Oswald' Mosey, leader of the MCC Junior Blackshirts, idly sucking at a half-digested domino. In the other corner sat the village statistician, the bearded Frindall, dozily and dreamily doing his impersonations of Mr Brian Johnston – and he wasn't being paid for them either.

Gooch, the village blacksmith, sat at the bar chomping silently and steadily at a horse shoe sandwich.

I ordered a pint of ale for myself, a small Babycham for Miss Roebuck and two meat and potato pies for both of us, and we sat at a plain-scrubbed table under the signed photographs of Mr Split Waterman and Miss Clare Francis, which were hard to tell apart with the naked eye.

Miss Roebuck sidled along the bench to my side and said:

'Do you know who we had in here last week?'

'No,' I said.

'Then I'll tell you. We had Christopher Martin-Jenkins and Neil Durden-Smith. They were standing there next to the bar skittles playing with each other's hyphens.'

It was peaceful and restful in the bar.

Don 'Sir Oswald' Mosey nodded off happily in the corner contentedly dunking his domino in his half-pint of condemned scrumpy.

Dear old Willum Frindall had been joined by

Squire Brearley's gardener, Titchmarsh, and together the two old notables were defacing the adverts in the current copy of *The Cricket Naturists' Weekly*.

The cherry on the top of Miss Roebuck's Babycham seemed to have loosened her tongue and as her voice grew louder and more animated she became quite indiscreet in her criticisms of the Festival Committee's programme of events for the coming season.

'We don't need another memorial horse trough,' she said. 'Surely to goodness Squire Brearley can find something else to drink his junket from. I tell you what we need. What we need is a memorial wireless mast.'

'I beg your pardon?' I said.

'We want the BBC – and the British Broadcasting Corporation as well – to put up a wireless mast on top of Botham's Gut so we can hear the ball-by-ball Test match commentaries on Radio 3. When they've got Haydn on, you can always hear him, but Trevor Bailey's totally inaudible. It's not fair. If they can't afford a proper mast what they should do is stick a spiked German First World War helmet on Brian Johnston's head and make him stand there for the whole of the cricket season.'

I raised my eyebrow doubtfully.

'It's all right,' she said. 'We'd feed him. We'd give him chocolate cakes and sticky buns and special fudge slices that Freddie Trueman could eat without taking his teeth out.

'We'd get all the village children to garland him with flowers and dance round him on midsummer's day like a maypole.

'We could draw murals on the top of his head

and give him the freedom of Droitwich. You never know, if we plugged him in properly, we might even be able to get Radio Hilversum.'

I nodded thoughtfully.

'The trouble is, they're so parochial here,' she said. 'Look what they've arranged for the village fete. Who's impressed by its being opened by Sir Neville Cardus? I'm not. Why couldn't we go for broke and ask Princess Di? I know she's got big feet, but she could always stay overnight at Squire Brearley's provided she promised not to use the lavatory first.

'And look at the rotten old entertainments they're providing. Who wants another demonstration of free fall parachuting by the MCC red and yellow devils? I'm sick of it. No one ever gets killed, do they?'

Her eyes began to water and a pink flush spread over her collar bones and glowed brightly on the bridge of her nose.

'There's so much we could do,' she said. 'I could embroider a special history of Witney Scrotum, I've got the patterns for it.

'I could do a special lantern slide lecture on the achievements of Viv Richards and Joel Garner. It wouldn't be expensive, because we could do it all in black and white, couldn't we?'

She downed her next glass of Babycham in a single gulp and to my alarm her voice grew more strident:

'We could burn down the Golf Ball Museum and we could have nude limbo dancing on the village green and we could have an over-eighties marathon with Cliff Richard and Ann Shelton and we could invite Imran Khan to do an exhibition of pig-sticking against Javed Miandad, and we could have rude video films of David Bairstow wearing his Yorkshire cricket cap back to front.'

By now I was beginning to get slightly alarmed by the nature of Miss Roebuck's behaviour.

Her neck was lolling to the right and her left shoulder was sagging towards her left hip, and I feared she was going to take up guard like Mr Peter Willey, formerly of the Northamptonshire County Cricket Club.

But no, even worse was to follow.

With a gasp, a clutch at her throat and a whirring of her Royal Doulton earrings she slid slowly from the bench and collapsed senseless at my feet.

At this moment the Brigadier and the Commodore entered the bar.

The Brigadier took a brief look at her, kicked her idly in the ribs and said:

'Drunk again. Snorters all round, is it?'

We concluded the session's drinking in most agreeable fashion, throwing dry cleaner's staples at Don 'Sir Oswald' Mosey and recounting slightly risqué rugger stories about the life and times of Mr Nigel Smarmer-Stiff.

Presently, time was called and we had to leave.

The Brigadier and the Commodore took hold of Miss Roebuck by the scruff of her neck, dragged her out of the public house and threw her without much ceremony into the boot of the trusty Lanchester.

We spent the rest of the evening yarning happily in the Commodore's summer-house about mutual friends and enemies, old railway branchlines approved by Mr O. S. Nock and Mr Egon Ronay, historic cricket pads and fountain pens of beloved memory.

We repaired to our respective beds in a warm glow of alcoholic concomitance.

Next morning I awoke stiff with cold.

My limbs ached.

My eyeballs rattled in ice-encrusted sockets.

Frost cracked in my beard and in the folds of . . .

And then I remembered.

I leapt out of bed.

I raced down to the garage.

I flung open the doors.

There were muffled cries from the boot of the Brigadier's trusty Lanchester.

I hurled it open.

Miss Roebuck emerged, dishevelled and rumpled, yet strangely, cool, calm and collected.

'And there's another thing we could do for the bicentenary,' she said.

'What?' I said hoarsely. 'What?'

'We could hire Viv and Joel to play next season for Witney Scrotum,' she said.

What a lovely, lovely lady, I thought.

Such a pity I'm already spoken for.

3

The Third Man

I HAD TO RETURN to London.

There were matters of an urgent domestic nature to attend to.

There was another outbreak of peeping toms in the neighbourhood, and the poodle was growing nervous and refusing to take a bath in the evenings.

Worse still, he had started growling at the shower curtain.

My wife was still locked in bitter dispute with her trombone repairer, and the parrot, for some reason known only to himself, had started to shout at the top of his voice:

'Sod Robin Bailey.'

And there was the mail:

Yet another begging letter from Mr Christopher Martin-Jenkins inviting me to contribute an article to yet another of his interminable anthologies.

This one was entitled: *The Bumper Book of Funny Cricket Stories of a Comical Nature that will Make You Want to Rock with Laughter*.

There was yet another circular from American Express inviting me to fly Concorde to Trent Bridge, returning by Orient Express to Old Trafford and thence by QE2 to Aigburth, Liverpool, where SS *Canberra* would enship us to Lord's with cabaret provided by the Lord's Taverners Sequence Dance Team, more than half of which was composed of Miss Judith Chalmers.

There was one bright spot, though – a letter from my contact in the household of the Royal Family (a defrocked scorer from Worcestershire CCC 2nd XI) informing me that to scenes of national fervour and rejoicing Mr Billy Connolly had at long last learned not to slurp his baked beans in the presence of Her Majesty the Queen at supper and was coming along quite nicely in his curtseying technique to Miss Pamela Stephenson.

And then there were the books to review.

I have always believed that it is the bounden duty of my fellow writers to flatter each other in the literacy columns of the more expensive newspapers and so, althought my eyesight is failing and my temper is growing shorter by the day, I have readily agreed to do my bit and take part in the noble crusade to insert Miss Jackie Collins and Mr Jasper Carrott at the top of the bestseller list in *The Sunday Times*.

Accordingly, I ran myself an extremely hot bath, immersed myself in it with a bottle of chilled Tizer and an unprimed hand grenade and commenced to flick through the titles of my latest batch.

What an inspiring list.

Among the books were:

Tales from a Green Room, Tales from a Smoke Room, Tales from a Locker Room, Tales from a Common Room, Tales from a Doctor's Waiting Room, Tales from a Dentist's Waiting Room, Tales from a Vet's Waiting Room, Tales from an Intensive Care Unit, Tales from a Delivery Room, Tales from a Paraplegic's Recreation Room, Tales from a Condemned Cell, Tales from a Battered Wives' Home, Tales from a Gay Lesbian and Shirt Lifters' One Parent Family Rehabilitation Centre, Tales from an Umpires' Rest Home, Tales from a Home for Distressed Publishers, Tales from a Distressed Literary Agent Looking for an Original Title for One of his Clients, Tales from a Sergeants' Mess, Tales from a Corporals' Mess, Tales from the Giles Gordon Highlanders, Tales from a Bus Shelter, Tales from a Tram Stop, Tales from a Sewerage Farm, Tales from Leo Cooper, Tales from Leo Cooper and Jilly Cooper, Tales from Leo Cooper, Jilly Cooper and their Children, Tales from Leo Cooper, Jilly Cooper, their Children and their Dogs, More Tales from Leo Cooper, Jilly Cooper, their Children and their Dogs, Tales from Witney Scrotum which is Written in a Slightly Different Style from the Above.

As always I was astounded by the wit, ingenuity and originality of my fellow authors, including Mr Tim Brooke-Taylor, who appeared to have written well over three-quarters of the titles.

I was just about to plug myself into my word processor to inform the literary editor of *The Homeo-pathic Cricketers' Monthly* of these opinions, when I was interrupted by a phone call.

It was from the Brigadier.

'Whatho, Vileness,' he said. 'I'm talking to you on the telephone.'

'I know,' I said.

'What's that? I can't hear you,' he bellowed. 'Put some more money in the machine.'

I made a series of metallic clinking noises with my tongue into the mouthpiece, and he grunted with satisfaction.

'That's better,' he said. 'Bloody new-fangled things. Keep them on their toes, I say. Always keep them guessing.'

And then he dropped his bombshell.

He wished me to return to Witney Scrotum immediately.

He had vital news to impart.

He would brook no excuse.

I had to travel to Witney Scrotum at once.

I explained the situation to my wife. To my surprise she raised no objections.

She was holding a series of Tupperware parties and beetle drives for the wives and sweethearts of MCC tourists currently being unfaithful in Australia.

She was holding a coffee morning on behalf of Help the Aged, with particular reference to Mr Raymond Illingworth, and there were emergency repairs to be done on her dado rails.

My absence from the house, she said, would not be missed.

Accordingly, I entrained the following morning at Paddington Station and settled myself in a compartment which, as always on this West Country line, seemed to consist entirely of ill-tempered, retired colonels of defunct cavalry regiments, drink-crazed rural deans and seriously unfulfilled naval architects.

I had with me a goodly supply of books culled from the aforementioned pile of review copies to present to the Brigadier, who was always appreciative of such gifts since the district mobile library had been converted to a canine beauticians' and senior citizens' sheltered home.

Among the volumes were:

Miss Margaret Drabble's *Under the Waterman*.

A beautiful book this, being a definitive history of speedway with a delicate and definitive account of the life and times of the eponymous Split, and an evocative analysis of the trailing leg technique of Mr Ollie Langford of Odsal.

There was *The Emlyn Hughes Book of How to Write Grammar Proper when you Speak it Out Loud*.

I read the blurb with interest.

'Mr Hughes has took two of television's most outstandingest and articulate commentators, Mr Mick Channon and Mr Ron Atkinson, who talk a lot, too, and has give examples of the way what they speak correct. You can have hours of endless fun using your crayons to colour in their litotes and hyperboles.'

I skimmed through the book I intended to lend to the Brigadier on my visit to Witney Scrotum, *The Martina Navratilova Charm Book*.

In it the scrumptious Martina had written: 'The best way to look charming is to wear a frock and shave under your armpits.'

The Brigadier would later append his own notes to the flyleaf: 'I tried it, and it made me look a bloody fool. I think she must be referring to chaps like the lady wife and her unmarried spinster sister.'

I picked up another book from the pile and there staring at me from the glossy dust jacket was a young man with an excess of teeth.

It was entitled *Sebastian Coe's Book of Injuries*, and I am bound to say it was an inspiring account of one man's heroic battle against a series of quite dreadful injuries suffered while doing television commercials. How noble the sacrifices he has made in the name of sport.

I was enchanted by *The ABC of Polo* by Princess Michael of Kent.

It was a pity she didn't know more of the alphabet (I must send her some gift vouchers for a Berlitz Course in Basic English). However, I did feel her own personal rags to riches story was an outstanding fable of modern times showing how she rose from serving cardboard cups of Bovril on the terraces at Wakefield Trinity to marrying some poor booby from the Royal Family whose name she quite often forgets – as indeed he does himself on not infrequent occasions.

As we hurtled through Reading I read with some pleasure *The Fight Of The Century*, an exciting blow by blow account of Fatima Whitbread's epic world heavyweight championship bout against Tim Witherspoon.

It took me a little longer to read *The Torvill and Dean Story*, the authorised history of the careers of Margaret Thatcher and Norman Tebbit, showing just how far you can go skating on thin ice.

I gathered that it was shortly to be made into a movie entitled *Escape from N'Tebbit*.

The train rattled happily over the points outside Didcot and I purred with satisfaction as I flicked through the pages of *Alliss in Wonderland*.

This was a reprint of the much-loved children's classic about the fantasy world of television sports commentators. All the old favourites were there – the magical moment when Harry Carpenter drops down the nineteenth hole at Turnberry, the hilarious tea party where Desmond Lynam falls off his moustache and David Coleman turns into a nice person and, of course, that memorable passage when Murray Walker actually gets a name right.

As the train thundered through Alston Low Level and the marshalling yards at Wolstenholme Halt I cast my eyes briefly over:

A Manual for One Parent Lesbian Golfers.

The Rhodes Boyson Book of Darts.

Hobdayed, Fired and Fetlocked – My Life with Jennie Pitman.

As always I marvelled at the breathtaking daring and breadth of vision of Britain's publishing houses and their noble battle to keep Miss Clare Francis from their lists.

Soon we reached Graveney Junction, where I was greeted warmly by the Brigadier and his oldest and closest friend, the Commodore.

The Brigadier smiled broadly.

'Whatho, Vileness,' he said. 'The lady wife's not here. She's away on manoeuvres with her unmarried spinster sister in Cheltenham. We'll have to forage for our own fodder. Still, at least it won't interfere with the old snorter activities, eh?'

He settled himself alongside me in the back seat of the Commodore's bottle green Humber and we clattered out of the station yard dragging behind us several segments of a bus shelter which had mysteriously attached itself to the rear fender.

The Brigadier was totally unaware of this.

Before the Commodore had had time to demolish the litter bins outside the Colonel Gadhaffi Takeaway Time Bomb Kabin he had pressed himself close to me and whispered into my ear:

'Vileness.'

'Yes,' I said.

'I have some fearfully important news to impart to you.'

'What?' I said, surreptitiously trying to remove a metal coat hanger which had mysteriously insinuated itself into the crutch of my corduroy trousers.

The Brigadier looked over his shoulder, cast his eyes round furtively and then whispered:

'I have discovered there is a mole in the MCC.'

'Good God,' I said. 'The Third Man.'

'He could be,' said the Brigadier. 'He could also be Leg Slip or Silly Mid Off for all I know. What's that got to do with it?'

He rattled his smoker's compendium testily and cracked his knuckles.

I was about to speak, but it was obvious to me he was reluctant to talk, and so in the snuff-stained darkness of the bottle green Humber with its debris of half-spent Maltesers and rotting nasal inhalers I had time to ponder in detail over the Brigadier's momentous statement.

Dear Lord, it was not two or three years since he had revealed to a stunned nation and a semi-comatose Mr Leo Cooper the identity of another mole who had wormed his way into the top echelons of power in the MCC as Keeper of the Queen's Cricket Erotica at Lord's and had for over forty years revealed this country's innermost secrets to the enemies beyond our shores.

He it was who had revealed during the immediate post-Munich days to von Ribbentrop (more commonly known as Mr Brian Sellers) the fact that Messrs Gunn and Moore were to introduce a totally new and revolutionary Eddie Paynter autograph eight-spring cricket bat with integral ukelele facility.

He it was who revealed to agents of the KGB during the darkest and bleakest days of Stalin's Cold War the top secret knitting patterns behind the sweaters of Northamptonshire County Cricket Club – small wonder, therefore, that Guy Burgess had been able to practise his treachery for so long under the guise of Romper Suit Editor of *Pins and Needles*.

He it was who had circulated to certain national newspapers compromising pictures of Queen Mary and the Princess Royal playing three card brag with Messrs Freddie Mills and Ivor Novello in the bike sheds at Bramall Lane.

And he it was who convinced Margaret Thatcher, the Ink Monitor at Number Ten, that Sir Anthony Blunt was a thoroughly decent, honest, upright chap, who for many years had played as hooker for Rochdale Hornets under the nom de plume 'A. N. Other' and had been the much valued partner of Mr E. M. Forster in innumerable Wimbledon Mixed Doubles Championships under the nom de plume of 'Lytton Strachey'.

His dastardly activities had only been cut short when he was apprehended attempting to smuggle through HM Customs and Excise at Dover Mr 'Bomber' Wells in the false bottom of a William Morris cricket bag.

God knows what damage he would have inflicted on the nation had his vile plan succeeded. Imagine the quality of life without dear old 'Bomber' taking his place in the centre of the line-up of the Beverley Sisters.

But now?

Now there was another mole.

I could scarcely contain myself as we entered the outskirts of Witney Scrotum.

The Brigadier, however, was not to be moved. His lips were sealed.

Not a sound did he make as the Commodore ripped up half the cattle grid outside the front door of Mrs Botham's Takeaway Home Perm and High-light Salon.

He shook his head silently and firmly when the Commodore invited us in for a supper of ship's biscuits and scurvy-free Ovaltine.

And then, within a short time, I found myself in his study drinking behind heavily bolted doors stiff draughts of home-distilled cough lozenge gin and eating the most delicious vol au vents of litmus paper and unused stamp hinges.

The Brigadier downed three glasses of gin in three single gulps and then launched into his story.

'Yes, Vileness,' he said. 'The worst has happened – we have another mole in the MCC.'

I shook my head in sympathy at his distress.

'Do you realise that for the whole of last season the selectors' committee room at Lord's was bugged?'

I gasped.

'Imagine it,' he said. 'The innermost secrets of Princess Peter May of Teck revealed to the enemy.'

'Crikey,' I said. 'Do you happen to know what colour underpants he wears?'

'Lime green with a red polka dot,' growled the Brigadier. 'No wonder that scum, Sir Robert Armstrong, looked so shifty in the witness box at Sydney.'

He stood up and commenced to prowl round the room.

He paused in front of his signed Lowry prints depicting the four seasons at Old Trafford cricket ground – winter, winter, winter and harshest and bleakest of all, summer.

The stuffed macaw, Dexter, gazed down at him with cynical, loveless eyes from the top of the hat stand, and he continued:

'Do you really think Sir Eric Hollies of Warwickshire was a spy?'

I shook my head.

'Well, that's what the Mole is putting around,' he said. 'Worse still, he's trying to convince *Wisden* that Chapman Snitcher once opened the innings for Minor Counties versus India.'

What foulness, I thought. What perfidy.

The Brigadier poured out two more glasses of gin and scratched his head thoughtfully.

'And yet . . . and yet . . . I can't help feeling that this creature is doing it for the best possible of motives. I've got this nagging, no this overwhelming feeling that he is doing it all for the love of our precious "summer game",' he said.

'What?' I gasped. 'What?'

The Brigadier smiled wanly.

'Let me explain, Vileness,' he said. 'When I look at the information he is providing there are certain elements which do seem to contain strong aspects of truth.'

He took out a tape cassette from the sporran of the kilt worn by Mr Mike Denness when batting against Lillee and Thomson at Melbourne, and held it up.

'This tape,' he said. 'The Mole claims it is a genuine recording from a BBC ball-by-ball commentary. Well, can we really be certain that it is indeed bogus?'

He pointed to a recording machine he had borrowed from Miss Roebuck the proprietress of the dog biscuit shop and said:

'Do you know how to work these confounded contraptions?'

I nodded.

'Well, play the tape and tell me what you think.'

After fifteen minutes I managed to extract the cassette from its plastic container and within the hour had accomplished its insertion into the machine ready for playing.

'You youngsters,' said the Brigadier. 'You really are dab hands with these modern inventions, aren't you? If you've got the time, I wonder if you'd show me how to work the lady wife's toenail clippers?'

I nodded.

Twenty minutes later I had succeeded in finding the 'Play' button on the machine. I pressed it with a certain amount of triumph, I have to confess, and we heard the following:

' "Well, Blowers, and what did you have for breakfast this morning?" '

' "Actually, my dear old thing, I had three lightly boiled quail's eggs, half a dozen oysters and . . . and a red London bus pulls away down Wellington Road and three seagulls pass lazily over the Mound stand and a covey of pigeons peck contentedly at long leg and . . . and then I had scrambled eggs and caviare followed by . . . oh, gosh, there's a wicket fallen."

' "Really, Blowers? Jolly interesting. And what did you have to drink?"

' "Half a bottle of chilled Borassa Valley hock with two twists of Dandanong passion fruit."

' "Jolly good. Well, that's England 76 for 7. Now then, Boil, what did you have for breakfast?"

' "Well, acksherlly, I had two bowls of All Bran, six stewed prunes, an Ex Lax sandwich with the crusts cut off . . . there's another wicket gone . . . a carton of skimmed soya bean yoghourt and half a mug of yeast extract, taste-free liquid Gregory Powder."

' "Jolly good, Boil. And I suppose you were well in the runs there. Oh golly, there's another gaffe. Well then, that's England 76 for 8 and needing 156 to avoid an innings defeat. Now then, Alderman. What about you? What did you have for breakfast?"

' "Bugger off."

' "Jolly good. Bearded Wonder – come on. Out with it. What did you have for brekkers this morning?"

' "One hundred and sixteen rice crispies, which is seven more than I had on the morning of 6 June, 1977, but five fewer than the cornflakes consumed by Maurice Tompkin on the morning of 2 July, 1947, when he scored 22, caught Edrich bowled Roberts, Leicestershire versus Lancashire, Melton Mowbray. That, by the way, was Edrich G. A."

' "Jolly interesting, Bearders. Well then, while you've been talking two more England wickets have fallen which means we're all out and have lost by an innings and 155 runs. So the match is over. Now then, what do we do next? I know. We'll have a slice of the delicious ginger parkin sent to us by a Miss Antonia Lewis of Porthcawl who says she'd give anything to be chief microphone duster in our commentary box." '

I nodded gravely.

'It seems authentic enough to me,' I said.

'Of course it is,' said the Brigadier. 'And that's why I am convinced that the man we are dealing with is a good mole, an inherently decent, god-fearing, patriotic mole.'

I shook my head, baffled and bewildered.

'How do you mean?' I said.

The Brigadier poured out more drinks and happily reamed his pipe, scattering specks of half-ignited charcoal over the fireside rug specially knitted for him from fragments of Mr Jimmy Greaves's moustache.

'I'll tell you,' he said. 'It explains totally why the government is seeking to ban publication of *Wisden* under the fifty years rule.'

'The fifty years rule?' I said.'

'Of course,' said the Brigadier. 'At last they think they've got the excuse to stop the publication of cricket records until half a century after they've been accomplished. Imagine it, Vileness. It won't be until at least the first decade of the twenty-first century, if they have their way, that the world knows officially that A. T. W. "Wally" Grout took eight catches, Queensland versus Western Australia, Brisbane, 1959.'

'But why?' I asked. 'Why?'

'Because I know the full story of the American business.'

'What American business?'

The Brigadier leaned forward, clapped his hand violently over my mouth and bellowed:

'Hush. Walls have ears. That's why it's so damnably difficult to stick anaglypta to them.'

He paused for a moment to finish his glass of gin laced liberally with a goodly portion of Sparkling Natural Yorkshire Dales Spring Water bottled in Saudi Arabia.

Then he continued:

'I'll tell you what really happened. It wasn't the Americans who shipped arms to Iran. It was our lot. The MCC. And it wasn't arms we shipped. Do you know what it was?'

'No,' I said. 'Tell me. Tell me.'

'It was a major consignment of stumpers' gloves, motorised, heavy rollers, Playfair cricket annuals and second-hand sightscreens from our beloved Bramall Lane. We also offered them Mr H. D. "Dicky" Bird, but they refused on grounds of public decency.'

My shins tingled with excitement. This was a story that even Mr Chapman Snitcher would be pleased to call his own – a major novelty of journalism indeed.

But there was more to come.

'And do you know where the money from the great deal went, my dear Vileness?' said the Brigadier.

'Where?' I asked. 'For God's sake, where?'

'To the Contras.'

'The Contras?' I said. 'In Nickerwhatshisname?'

'No, you bloody idiot – Yorkshire,' said the Brigadier. 'The money went to the Contra Rebels in Yorkshire County Cricket Club to finance the fight to bring back Boycott.'

'Crikey,' I said.

The Brigadier nodded in sombre fashion.

'Thus are the highest ideals of a nation subverted,' he said. 'There's also money in the pipeline to pay for the Somerset rebels, too. Who do you think paid for Botham to go to Worcestershire?'

Soft owls hooted. Hedgehogs snuffled in deep-rutted ditches. Winter-bound county cricket scorers furtively oiled the castors of their Frindall patent portable commodes.

And then the Brigadier smiled. He smiled and he began to laugh.

'But the greatest thing of all he has revealed is the issue, on which the whole nation can unite and take its final glorious stand, fighting with all its might and all its main,' he said.

'And what issue's that?' I said.

'The government's plans to privatise the MCC.'

Of an instant the blood curdled in my veins. My God, we'd already lost British Gas and the Post Office Directory Enquiries. Was it possible that another blow even more mortal would be struck against the very vitals of our heritage and our cherished way of life?

'Oh yes,' said the Brigadier. 'The Ink Monitor's absolutely determined to sell off the MCC.

'The Mole himself personally told me of her plans.

'She's going to turn the Pavilion at Lord's into a multi-purpose leisure complex for Arabs. There'll be a casino in the long room, separate dressing-rooms for home and visitors' call girls and a special grovelling room where Mrs Thatcher can debase herself personally in front of minor Saudi princelings for television programmes that have displeased them.

'She's going to convert the indoor batting school into special hangars for Cruise missiles and a repository for Norman Tebbit's underpants.

'The Mound stand she's going to turn into an official annexe of the White House so she can be nearer to Nancy Reagan when they want to swap knitting patterns and incontinence prescriptions.

'And the square, my dear Vileness? The square will be ripped up and replaced by a yachting marina with facilities for synchronised dancing and the ritual drowning of unwanted cabinet ministers.'

I was aghast.

My cheeks turned pale and my eyes grew bloodshot.

'But what about the members?' I said. 'What will happen to them?'

'Oh, she's got plans for them, old boy,' said the Brigadier. 'She's going to privatise old age, you see, so they'll be part of that.'

'Privatise old age?' I said.

'That's right,' said the Brigadier. 'She's got rid of the butter mound. Now she's going to get rid of the old people mound.'

'How?'

'Ship them off to the Falklands. Plenty of room for them there. Give the soldiers a change shooting senior citizens instead of the penguins.'

The Brigadier smiled when he saw the look of horror that had flooded over my face.

'Do not be downhearted, my friend,' he said. 'Here is your greatest moment. Here is your chance to emblazon your name across the weft and warp of our national life. Here is your chance to go down in the annals as the man who saved our beloved "summer game".'

I opened my mouth to speak, but the Brigadier bellowed:

'Go. Go this instant. And remember to put paper in the machine this time.'

I walked to the door.

My senses quickened. I felt a heady excitement. Gosh, if I played my cards right I could find myself dizzily scaling the pinnacles of journalism in the company of the all-time greats, Gilbert Odd, Basil V. Easterbrook and the immaculate 'Backstop' of the *Rangoon Weekly Clarion and Trumpeter*.

At the door I paused.

'There's just one thing,' I said.

'Yes?' said the Brigadier.

'Who is the Mole?'

The Brigadier tapped the side of his nose slowly.

'On that score I plead the fifth amendment,' he said. 'However, I do seem to recall his telling me he'll be doing *Down Your Way* from Congleton next Sunday week.'

4

Souvenirs

AT TIMES of great national rejoicing – royal weddings involving people with big ears and bald patches, state visits by members of the Tongan royal family, the birthday of Sir Richard Attenborough, the marriage of Miss Carole Thatcher to someone involving big ears and bald patches, the bicentenary of Witney Scrotum, the jubilee of the establishment of Lord's as a rest home for retired admirals and Mr Neil Durden-Smith – my thoughts always turn to matters of a deep and profound nature.

Why, for example, have postmen ceased to wait at your front door to deliver a parcel?

One sharp rap at the knocker, one perfunctory ring at the bell, and they're off.

They do not hang about.

You bellow at the top of your voice:

'Wait! Wait! I'm coming. Leave it on the mat.'

You stagger downstairs, tripping over the standard poodle, cracking the glass on the Helen Bradley print with the point of your elbow.

The cord of your dressing-gown is sodden and dripping through sudden and unexpected immersion in the lavatory basin, and minute screws come spurting out of the rims of your spectacles.

Your heart is pumping, dried sleep claws at your eyeballs, your big toenail snags a hole in the stair carpet and the parrot starts to mimic the telephone.

'I'm coming, I'm coming,' you shriek. 'For the love of God leave it on the mat.'

But, no, when you get to the front door, the swine has gone.

You can feel his leer lingering among the milk bottles and the bay tree that needs watering.

And sticking through the letter box is a large card informing you that the delivery officer(delivery officer, for pete's sake) was unable to deliver a parcel/package, and after reading at least eighty-seven paragraphs and subsections and addenda and amendments you realise you are invited to present yourself at your nearest sorting office to collect the said parcel/package.

Thus it was two days ago, on a blissful urban early summer's morning of sleet, incipient hail and cloying, billowing car exhaust fumes, that I walked the three and a half miles to my nearest sorting office to collect the parcel/package which my friendly neighbourhood delivery officer had been unable to deliver.

'Got your card, have you?' said the clerk, who incidentally bore a marked resemblance to Mr Allan Lamb on a good day at Kettering.

I looked at him blankly.

He spoke again.

The walk home was through light flurries of snow which, by the time I had rescued the card from the kitchen pedal bin, wiped off the fragments of marmalade, cat food and pilchards in tomato sauce and returned once more to the sorting office, had developed into stinging needles of gale-whipped hail which turned my ears inside out and stiffened the fringes of my Finnish army winter muffler.

I am bound to say, however, that the arduous enterprise was well worth the rigours and the dangers.

For on returning home and opening the parcel/packet there was revealed to me a treasure trove of delights and marvels, which I am only too pleased to share with you, dear readers.

First appeared a letter from the Brigadier, written in green ink with steel-nibbed pen.

It read thus:

Whatho, Vileness.

My regards to your parrot and I trust your skin complaint has improved since last we met.

Take my advice. Bathe daily in alum, eschew all contact with members of the Household Cavalry and never fail to change your socks weekly.

Is London as loathsome as ever?

Does the moving Underground Railway system still reek of reindeer droppings?

Do the ladies of the night still look like Leslie Compton wearing women's togs?

Is that stinker, Lord Baden-Powell, still holding his ghastly jamborees in Hyde Park?

No matter, Vileness.

There are issues of much greater import to consider and ponder over.

I beg you to examine carefully the enclosed documents. They are the proofs of the Witney Scrotum bicentenary programme and brochure, edited by Miss Roebuck from the dog biscuit shop and printed by dear old Bruce Woodcock of *The Times* on his Rupert Murdoch patent computerised John Bull printing set.

I earnestly commend them to your attention and ask you for considered comments on same.

Kindly write these in capital letters on the thin-lined notepaper and remember to affix a valid postage stamp to the envelope.

I remain,

Yours etc, etc.

I unsealed the inner package, carefully wrapped in back numbers of *The Sporting Chronicle* and *Dalton's Weekly*, and there were presented to my eager eyes joys and felicities unbounded.

Let me repair to my study, beat back the standard poodle, sweep up the half-sucked millet sprays, pour myself a stiff Bovril and Complan, and I shall describe to you what I found in that package.

There are times of quivering enchantment and bewitching magic, as when you first open the latest and seventy-sixth volume of the official autobiography of Sir Geoffrey Boycott.

There are moments of breathtaking, awesome anticipation, as when you read the first page of Miss

Jilly Cooper's *Anthology of the Volvo Estate* and realise that she is indeed almost as much as she is cracked up to be.

There is the intense satisfaction of witnessing the recent onset of puberty in Mr Matthew Engels of *The Manchester Guardian*.

But there was nothing to compare with my first sight and subsequent perusal of the Witney Scrotum memorial programme and brochure.

How skilful the make-up, with scarcely a headline upside down and the barest minimum of spelling mistakes.

How subtle the design, with every page numbered consecutively, with only the last twenty-seven faintly indecipherable, having either been written in Urdu or printed by dear old Bruce Woodcock during a long and lonely session at his Longparish home-made corn plaster gin.

I particularly liked the advertisements.

On the front page of the brochure in full colour black and white monochrome was the most superbly contrived invitation to join The Folio Society and accept a free introductory gift of a volume of the delicious, witty and ravishing Miss Frances Edmunds entitled: *Another Bloody Poseur or The Truly Remarkable Histories of the Nine Lives of Mr Desmonde Morrisse and His Celebrated Tomes on Dog Watching, Bed Wetting and Cannibalism among the Wives of Crickette Tourists with Subsequent Accounts of his Numerous and Informative Appearances on Moving Television Chat Shows to Promote Same*.

I resolved there and then to fill in my application form without delay and send my presentation volume to the saintly Sir David Attenborough who is patently totally ignorant of such matters of a zoological and anthropological nature.

Turning the pages, I came upon more advertisements which thrilled me to the core.

What a perfect mixture of the famous and the mundane, the glamorous and the homely.

There, facing the glossy, brilliantly tinted, full page advert for Gucci surgical underwear was a simple, home-drawn notice, reading thus:

'Contact Mrs Botham, for home-made, handknitted country-craft cricket sweaters. All clubs and counties undertaken, provided it's not Somerset.

'Also personalised crotcheted odour eaters and Fair Isle toupées as worn by Mr Geoffrey Boycott.'

I flicked on through the pages.

It was just like the *Sunday Times* colour magazine; only the staples didn't drop out when you read it in the bath.

All the great names of industry and commerce were there. All those giants who bring a stirring and coursing of patriotic pride to our true blue English blood – Alfa Romeo, Honda, Nissan, Lancia, Renault, Sony, Knorr, Findus Frozen Firelighters and cordless Toblerones.

If I had had a mind, I could there and then in the relative comfort of my own home have filled in coupons to purchase a Laura Ashley Alpine bivouac, join the Readers' Union Sado-Masochist Book Club and enrolled as a boy soldier with the SDP–Liberal Alliance.

And yet holding their own among these thorough-breds were the simple announcements from the Brigadier's beloved Witney Scrotum.

'Visit the Witney Scrotum Golf Ball Museum.

'Special bicentenary exhibition of gutta percha inflatable Peter Alliss dolls with authentic smirk and leg hair.

'Edible food provided by trained cook who keeps herself spotless.

'First aid services in constant attendance.'

And:

'Fancy a bit of a piss-up? Come and have a good old thrash and sesh at Farmer Emburey's untreated scrumpy parlour.

'Free entry to the nightly honking competition.'

And:

'For dainty cream teas untouched by human hand visit old Grannie Swanton's emergency tea rooms.

'Sample her delicious Zube and Lemsip tartlets and her noted thigh pad pie in gymslip sauce.

'First aid services in constant attendance.'

And:

'Special guided tour of the village conducted by experts who seldom get lost and know how to read maps.

'Visit old Squire Brearley in his natural environs – feeding time twelve noon till two. Writing of incredibly learned articles for *The Sunday Times*, Thursdays eight a.m. till midnight.

'Pause a while at the mobile chiropodists and homeopathic dentistry and check your mouth for gum boils and ingrowing toenails.

'Purchase your sachet of natural laxatives at the dog biscuit shop and take your own individual brass rubbings of Don "Sir Oswald" Mosey.

'First aid services etc, etc.'

There was much more to admire, but then all of a

sudden my eyes boggled, glinted and then sparkled with exultation when I came to the section headed:

'Congratulations to Witney Scrotum.'

Here was page after page of messages of goodwill sent to the cricket club by personages famous and humble from all walks of life and from all corners of the globe.

I quote just a few:

Miss Jilly Cooper

'How super! I simply adore cricket. It's so sexy, isn't it? All those handsome, long-limbed, sun-bronzed young men in their tight white trousers and droopy hats. (I hope nothing else about them droops.)

Leo loves cricket, too. I think he's written a book about it.

When he starts talking about bowling maidens over and showing fine legs and doing the most unimaginable things with his short leg I go all weak at the knees and have these frightful fantasies about romping under the covers in nothing but my Barbour Coat with David Gower and those dark rings under his eyes.

Why do people always keep mistaking me for one of the Beverley Sisters?'

Prince Philip

'My heartiest congratulations to you all.

As I always say, when you play cricket, one knows you are playing a game that is quintessentially English born, bred and nurtured – just like me if you ignore my antecedents.

Cricket!

How pure and chaste and yet unsullied by the

multifarious malaises that make our contemporary society so beastly – nancy boy footmen at Buckingham Palace, darkies reading the news on television, slant-eyed brother Chink forever celebrating his bloody boring New Year, anti-pheasant and partridge slaughterers, so-called intellectuals giving away this nation's vital secrets in articles in the *Radio Times*, pacifists, Australian prime ministers, Mr Kipling Bakewell tarts, Royal Marine drop-outs, leftie BBC radio producers who keep going over to the Open University just when you want to listen to those bloody idiots making fools of themselves in *Today in Parliament*, Princess Michael of the Huns and that drippy husband of hers with the beard that smells of vintage cars and old cinemas, arty-farty layabouts who keep whinging for money for Andrew Previn and his band and those play things they put on at the National Theatre, those hordes of gormless drones from the North of England constantly grumbling and grousing about being unemployed – why can't they get on their coaches and four and find gainful employment like I do? You don't have to be bald to be President of the World Wild Life Fund, you know.

But that's just typical of the attitude these days, isn't it? There's a cottage industry of people taking the piss out of me. Why? I'm just an ordinary sort of bloke who likes going on royal visits to China and taking luxury cruises on HMS *Britannia* – and I gave my life for my country in the Second World War.

Enough of that. If I go on like this, I'll get a right royal bollocking from you-know-who.

So back to cricket.

Congratulations.
I'm thrilled to little shit bags for you.'

Andrew Lloyd-Webster
'Sarah has most graciously given me permission to send you her personal congratulations on your bicentenary, which, she tells me after looking in her dictionary, is two hundred years.

She wishes me to inform you that like herself you have become a national institution – although speaking for myself I don't think you can possibly be as tone deaf as she is.

She also expresses her desire to enclose an autographed full-length picture of herself wearing the hideous mask and make-up she uses in the show I helped her write, entitled *Phantom of the Opera*.

Incidentally, she is in such a good mood that I think she might slip me enough pocket money to buy a new velvet jacket, in which the sleeves won't be too long for me.

Marti Webb sends her love, too.'

Mr E. W. Swanton
'My felicitations and infinite blessings to you all.

Two hundred years of existence!

Well done. It is almost as long as I have been writing incredibly boring cricket articles for the *Daily Telegraph*. But no more – not since they've appointed that little squirt Max Jaffa as editor-in-chief.

Two hundred years! It seems almost as long as a luncheon spent in the company of Mr Alec Bedser and Mr Peter May.

Two hundred years! What profound changes I have witnessed during the span of those two centuries. As Archbishop of Canterbury I have officiated at twenty-seven royal weddings and funerals and been personally responsible for the canonisation of Billy J. Kramer and the Dakotas.

As Governor-General of India I was present at the birth of Mr Sunil Gavaskar (who incidentally hasn't grown an inch since that great day), and I oversaw and supervised the partition of Earl Mountbatman.

I can't quite think what I got up to when I was Pope – I hope at the very least I put the Wops in their place.

So, dear friends at Witney Scrotum, here's to the next two hundred years – surely to God they'll take off *The Price Is Right* before then?'

Mr Neil Kinnock
'Does the Right Honourable Lady have the effrontery and the gall to stand up in this House and maintain and aver and indeed state to Right Honourable and Honourable members that neither she nor her government had no knowledge of, hand in, responsibility for or cognisance of the selection of the MCC team to tour Australia during the past winter and that furthermore the raid on Lord's by members of the Special Branch was not a direct and immediate and, indeed, deliberate result of . . .

Ooops, sorry.

Wrong speech.'

Henry Blofeld
'My dear old things – oodles and oodles of congratters and all that sort of rot.

Actually I don't normally talk like that, you know.

71

Oh no. In fact, I'm quite a gloomy sort of chap really. Left to myself I talk in monosyllabic grunts and I become quite speechless and blush to the roots in the presence of ladies with nail varnish and big bosoms.

To tell the truth, I'm a raging bloody depressive.

Well, wouldn't you be?

What a miserable life I lead. All I've got to look forward to is travelling the world staying in expensive hotels and gentlemen's clubs, drinking exquisite wines, eating gourmet food and watching cricket while everyone back home's laid low with flu and piles during a typical English winter.

God, the boredom of it all. The misery!

Sitting next to Bill Frindall day after day in the commentary box at Lord's – can you think of a torture more damnable than that? Unless it's when I'm mistaken for one of the Beverley Sisters.

I wish I were a long distance lorry driver.

I wouldn't mind being a British Telecom engineer or a teacher of metalwork in the Black Country.

Sometimes in moments of the bleakest despair I have these ghastly nightmares of being Mr Tony Lewis.'

Mrs Margaret Thatcher

'Rejoice, gentlemen, rejoice. But not too much – we've got your ground earmarked for one of our lovely new nuclear power stations.

Look. Let me say here and now – I know nothing of these plans. Categorically nothing.

You can blame the Attorney General or the Minister of Defence or my Press Secretary or anyone you care to mention.

I can state here and now, hand on heart, that I was away on holiday when they will be discussed in Cabinet in the future.'

Ian Botham
'Like I say, roll on, eh? Bloody rotate. Fantastic. Like I say, bloody marvellous. Terrific.

Here's a copy of my latest book for your raffle. Like I say, I wrote it myself. All of it. Including the difficult bits with long words.

Like I say, roll on, eh? Bloody rotate.'

Harold Pinter
'Very good.'
  (Pause)
  'Yes.'
  (Pause)
  'Very good indeed.'
  (Pause)
  'It makes you think.'
  (Pause)
  'Yes indeed, it makes you think.'
  (Long pause)
  'Which is more than most of my plays do.'

Brian Johnston
'Well done, Witters.

Jolly good, Scroters.

Please find enclosed a bicentenary chocolate fudge cake with walnuts and almonds, angelica and damson jam filling and specially iced by Trevor Bailey's mother, the delicious Pearl.

Sorry about the state of the glacé cherries – we

caught Fred Trueman sucking the living daylights
out of them in the gents urinals at Trent Bridge.'

**Jimmy Saville, OBE, DFC and Bar, MC, VC, Iron
Cross, PhD (Open University with Distinction in
Difficult Sums), Order of Lenin, RAC, RSVP and
MCC**
'Sorry I couldn't fix it, but as it happens W. G.
Grace wasn't available at the time.
   We'll try the old bugger for the next series.
   Okay, pal?'

The President of MCC
'All at headquarters send to you our profoundest
congratulations on the attainment of your "double
ton".
   You might not be aware of the fact, but we, too,
have achieved a similar landmark in our history.
   You and your friends are cordially invited to
attend our jubilee hop to be held in the pavilion at
Lord's on midsummer's day.
   Music will be provided by Frankie Goes to Hollywood and Nigel Goes to Grace Road, Leicestershire.
   My committee have further asked me to send you
the enclosed brochure of souvenirs and mementoes
to celebrate the occasion and offer you one third
discount on all items displayed.'

What a beautiful and stimulating catalogue it was,
dear readers.
   I shall delve into it briefly and give just a few
examples of the many goodies on offer.
   'The most comprehensive selection of the world's
most famous cricket pavilions modelled at half scale

in a specially numbered edition and made from genuine hand-crafted Tupperware. Guaranteed dishwasher proof.'

And:

'Souvenir pyjama cases, ladies' leotards and gents' non-stick underpants in authentic non-run MCC colours with matching oven gloves. For all orders over one hundred a special free gift of Sir Pelham Warner – if stocks available.'

And:

'Bottles of genuine air, specially gathered from the Long Room at Lord's, complete with brandy fumes, stale cigar smoke and post-prandial farts from the aristocracy.'

And:

'A selection of rainwear, spats and tram drivers' gauntlets designed by Zandra Harold Rhodes from the the covers at the Nursery End.'

And:

'Presentation gift pack of the Wellington Road turnstiles in finest Royal Doulton pottery. Limited number of impolite, elderly gatekeepers without small change also available.'

And finally:

'Specially commissioned long-playing record: "The Sound of Lord's."

'Included in this unique collection are the celebrated: "Oh well played, sir. Well played." And:

' "Here we go, here we go, here we go."

And the justly celebrated:

' "Who's that black bugger with the arms reaching down to his ankles?" '

I wrote back to the Brigadier immediately:

'Tremendous.

'Put me down for a sesh at old Farmer Emburey's and the ladies' invitation tango with Miss Jilly Cooper at the Lord's jubilee hop.'

Knowing my luck, I shall end up doing the hokey cokey with Leo Cooper and Mr H. D. 'Dicky' Bird.

5

Tour de Force

WHEN I RETURNED next to Witney Scrotum spring
was in the air.

Gooch, the village blacksmith, had grown another
set of teeth, and was busily sharpening them on the
side of the horse trough outside the Baxter's Arms.

The village policeman, cheery, bucolic PC Jesty,
had garlanded the end of his bicycle pump with
streamers of gaily coloured tissue paper and tassles
of sprout tops.

Wheatears on passage to the distant hills and
moors of the north rested wearily in the water
meadows at Cowdrey's Bottom.

There were the first signs of new growth on
Farmer Emburey's best pork pie trilby.

And the village, preening itself silkily in the
honey gold sunshine, looked superb.

The cricket pavilion sparkled proudly in its new coat of paint.

The weather cock high on the spire of the church of St Kevin de Keegan, the patron saint of endorsements, puffed out its chest at the gentle breezes drifting in from the Mendis Hills.

And old Grannie Swanton's leggings positively gleamed under their new coat of dubbin and whitewash.

I had not been in the village long before I was accosted by a flushed and excited Miss Roebuck from the dog biscuit shop.

'Guess what?' she said. 'Oh, do guess what?'

'What?' I said.

'The Australians are coming to play here.'

'You what?' I said.

'It's true, it's true,' she fluted in her weak little high-pitched voice. 'They're coming here to play the village team on the day of the bicentenary.'

The mother of pearl necklace rattled uncontrollably on the front of her pale blue angora jumper. The hem of her Welsh tweed skirt quivered. The rollers under her black chiffon head scarf whirred and clattered.

'All those lovely hairy men coming to visit us,' she sighed. 'If Miss Denning butts in and tries to steal my thunder, I'll scratch her eyes out.'

A look of panic came to her eyes, and then she began to shake from top to bottom.

I calmed her by the application of a swift kick to her right shin and after taking a deep and vigorous inhalation of her vegetarian smelling salts she continued:

'It's old Squire Brearley who's done it. Apparently

78

he's quite well known in cricketing circles. He once served as Phil Edmunds' personal baggage master and it's through that and his other contacts in the Lord's Debating Society the Australians are coming.

'Oh gosh, do you think Alan Border will notice me? Do you think I should get my teeth capped? Do you think they'll stay on for the hop after the match and that gorgeous, dishy Dean Jones will ask me to dance in the ladies' invitation?'

Prodger the poacher passed us and exposed himself with a friendly nod of the head. But Miss Roebuck did not notice. She was lost in her reveries and as I left her I heard her muttering under her breath:

'Please, God, please, please don't let me have impetigo on the great day.'

That night the Brigadier, the Commodore and I were entertained to supper by old Squire Brearley.

As the wine flowed and the hours ticked by our talk turned to matters of a nostalgic nature.

The Commodore regaled us with stories of his days serving as a snottie on a monitor in the Yalu River.

The Brigadier told us of the harsh days of his boyhood in Burma, where his father was Director General of Net Practice for Dissident Hill Tribesmen.

And old Squire Brearley, gently tugging at his beard, softly recounted the happy days of his youth when he played conkers with Wittgenstein and shared his wine gums with Bertrand Russell and his son, Eric, who later achieved considerable fame as a forceful opening batsman for Middlesex.

And then in the early hours the talk, quite naturally, came round to cricket.

Memories of famous matches and famous cricketers came flooding back to us.

The wine loosened my tongue and I grew ecstatic in praise of the giants of my youth – the great and saintly Winston Place and his lazy and lissome late cut; Alan Barlow, munching pork pies at the back of the pavilion at Old Trafford; the immortal Willie Watson, golden-haired and lithe and stroking the ball to every corner of Bramall Lane; Roy Tattersall, crinkly-haired, straight-backed, right arm furled up behind his shoulders, spinning out the men from Derbyshire at Aigburth; Ken Grieves and his swooping catches close to the wicket; Bob Berry, Cliff Gladwin and the incomparable, the immortal J. B. Statham.

We all had our nonpareils among nonpareils, and as the conversation grew more animated we decided to compile our list of cricketers past and present on a tour of the world's cricketing countries.

And so here is our anniversary touring party to celebrate the bicentenary of Witney Scrotum Cricket Club.

The arguments were long and fierce in its compilation, but with the Brigadier as arbiter and writer of the accompanying notes I think it is worthy of perusal.

The captain:
Mr W. H. Wooller of Cambridge University and Glamorgan In my unprejudiced opinion every cricketer who has ever donned the noble sweater of Glamorgan County Cricket Club has contributed

more to the sum of the world's happiness than the whole bang shoot of belching, belly-aching, wife-beating, foul-breathed scum who inhabit the House of Commons.

And without a shadow of a doubt the noblest of all these noble cricketers is Mr Wilfred Wooller.

And so, without a second's hesitation, I nominate this paragon of all the cricketing (and non-cricketing) virtues, this pillar of society, this thorough-going good egg and brick as skipper of the party and bugger the claims of Miss Dorothy Tutin.

Humble to a fault, modest and retiring, unfailingly courteous, self-effacing, soft-spoken and a born diplomat, he has an abundance of all those qualities needed for the arduous and gruelling task of leading his men through the wild outbacks of Dagoland, the fetid, flip-flopped urban jungles of Down Under and the cider-crazed fleshpots of rural Somerset.

No man in the history of our beloved 'summer game' has received greater love from his fellow cricketers.

Adored by umpires, worshipped by journalists, sanctified in some of the more remote regions of the upper Swansea Valley, the affection and esteem in which he is held place him head and shoulders above his rivals.

And there are indeed many of these:

Here we think of Warwick 'Big Ship' Armstrong, of Sir Leonard 'Barbara' Hutton, of the Blessed Rayond Illingworth, of the dashing and debonair Ken Cranston, of Jardine and Noble, of Melville and Bradman, of the quiet, painfully shy Brian Close, of that utterly loathsome brute, Ian Chappell, and his equally detestable brother, Greg.

But all these are mere pygmies cowering timorously in the shadows cast by that colossus of the crimson rambler and the flashing willow, the Rev. Wilfred Ontong-Wooller.

Such is the overpowering modesty and goodness of this man that during the whole of his career in the first-class game he kept secret the fact that apart from being captain and secretary of our most precious and cherished Glamorgan County Cricket Club and honorary foster father to Mr Tony Cordle he was also founder and leader of the Sunday Day League One-Day Revivalist Evangelical Church in Wales.

Dropping both the 'Ontong' and the 'Rev.' from his name, he laboured assiduously and in complete secrecy for the many worthy causes 'dear to his heart'.

Among these were the Alec Skelding Home for Distressed Umpires, the annual BBC *Blue Peter* appeal for battered county cricketers and the International Relief Fund for the Gelding of West Indian Fast Bowlers.

I first met 'Taffy', as he likes to be called, on a blissful summer's afternoon in 1948 at the incomparably beautiful and exquisite St Helen's ground at Swansea.

In the far distance the waters of the bay glistened and sparkled, small coasters dipped and curtsied, and a Campbell's steamer gently and with infinite delicacy demolished three-quarters of Mumbles Pier.

The great man himself was sitting cross-legged at

the foot of the pavilion steps, smiling radiantly as he fashioned balsa wood effigies of Mr Len Muncer, which he distributed with a benign nod of his dear old shaggy head to the ragged urchins of Cymdonkin who flocked in homage at his feet.

On closer inspection I saw he was sitting on a bed of nails and half-digested laver bread sandwiches.

I smiled as I passed en route to the pavilion bar, and as I did so I heard him speak those immortal words, whose Celtic lilts and cadences have engraved themselves indelibly on his nation's cultural treasure chest:

'Hold on, butt. Are you a member by here?'

I hesitated.

It was my undoing.

Before I could inform him that I was a visiting member he had clapped me in irons, thrown me into the dungeons at the rear of the indoor batting school and was halfway through pulling out the toenails on my left foot, when I managed through my howls of agony to blurt out my identity.

He examined my membership card carefully.

He held it up to the light.

He sniffed it.

He tested the corners with his teeth.

He bathed it with alum and rubbed it with litmus paper.

He sent it by special despatch rider to Somerset House and instructed Fabian of the Yard to interrogate the lady wife back in Witney Scrotum.

Finally, he said:

'Just checking, my old butt. Just checking.'

'Well, you can't be too careful these days, isn't it?'

And thus began a friendship which has survived all the hardships and vicissitudes of the intervening years.

No one knows more than I the sacrifices he has made during his long devotion to the 'summer game' – the joys of motherhood being the greatest of all.

My admiration for him knows no bounds.

As a loving, caring human being he has no equal.

As a leader of men he has no peer.

What a pity he was such a bloody awful cricketer.

The Batsmen:
The Rev. Ernest J. Toteligh Barton of Witney Scrotum Cricket Club and Bible Society Casuals This was a unanimous choice.

This founding father of the 'summer game' was born in the remote Lancashire village of Cardus-in-Tyldesleydale in 1787, the exact year as the founding of Witney Scrotum Cricket Club.

He died at the bowler's end in Witney Scrotum one hundred years later, having just run seven to complete his century against Thirteen Warehousemen from Langridge-on-Sea.

The tragedy of a career cut short in its prime remains with us to this very day in our village, and every year on the anniversary of his death the dartboard is unhooked from his memorial plaque in the village hall and a short address is given by the vicar on an appropriate subject. Last year he delivered a most informative and amusing speech on the problems of rodent control.

'Totters', as he is known to his legions of admirers, was a dashing and forceful right-hand bat, the first clergyman to abandon the under-arm sermon and the father of twenty-three children of assorted sex and age.

His longevity both on the cricket field and in the nuptial bed was much admired.

His untimely death was said to have been caused by contact with an untreated cricket ball during Harvest Festival.

He was survived by his Airedale terrier.

Charles Bannerman of New South Wales and Australia
No, he didn't invent shirts for Marks and Spencer.

He was, in fact, the first man to score a Test century.

My God, how I envy him.

If only I held that record, my life would be complete.

Never mind painting 'Le Déjeuner sur l'Herbe'.

Never mind inventing elastoplast or winning the senior TT race at the Isle of Man.

Never mind driving a 'Super Claude' locomotive from Liverpool Street to Yarmouth or winning a fridge-freezer on the Bob Monkhouse quiz game on the moving television.

It is my opinion that any man 'worthy of his salt' would go to his grave happy and contented in the knowledge that he was the scorer of the first century in the history of Test cricket.

It took place on a typical high summer's day in Melbourne in the March of 1877.

A wicked chill wind was blowing straight off the Antarctic. Sleet and snow whipped the summits of the Dandanong Hills and South Yarra was overrun by marauding, starving gangs of penguins and Abos.

Charlie Bannerman batted all day against the fearsome might of the England bowling and when stumps were drawn was 126 not out.

Next day he continued to bat with savage brilliance and had scored 165 when a bumper from Ulyett split his finger and forced him to retire.

No one else in the side scored 20.

The Australians launched a public subscription for this great feat and presented him with £165.

Isn't that bloody typical of the Aussies?

The mean, selfish brutes were too busy spending their money pouring vast quantities of their foul, weak beer down their disgusting gullets to spare a copper for one of the greatest cricketers of all time.

Good God, only last year I myself personally 'shelled out' a good 10p for the Save Jack Simmons for the Nation appeal.

Sir Leonard Hutton of Yorkshire and England
I don't care what the record books say.

To me he is still undisputed holder of the record for the world's highest Test score – to wit 364 against the Australians at The Oval, 1938.

On that issue I will brook no further discussion.

I once saw Sir Leonard buying a copy of *Dalton's Weekly* on the station at Graveney Junction.

Later he was to become father of that incomparable Renaissance man, Richard Hutton, poet, explorer, big game hunter, historian, landscape gardener, balloonist, private tutor to Mr H. D. 'Dicky' Bird, lieder singer, Battle of Britain pilot, surgeon, racing car driver, water colourist, Alpinist, ballet master extraordinaire, escort of Princess Margaret, single-handed yachtsman, diarist, bon viveur, and mother of Cilla Black.

He is also a famous practical joker.

Once, while attending a match involving Northamptonshire, the great man stole a county cap from the team and, stooping his shoulders, donning a false moustache and taking rapid, shuffling steps on his knees, marched out to the wicket.

This prompted that eminent wit and scholar Dr Frederick Sewards Trueman to remark: 'Well, it's either Toulouse bloody Lautrec or Hutton dressed as Lamb.'

Hasn't cricket got such a wonderful fund of funny stories?

N. V. H. Riches of Glamorgan

Norman Riches once visited Witney Scrotum in 1911 on the memorable day when our county played its first and only Minor Counties championship match on our beloved ground.

He was playing for Glamorgan, who had not then been elevated to first-class status.

It was the first time I had ever seen Welshmen 'in the flesh' and it made a deep impression on me as they massed in front of the pavilion singing 'Cwm Rhondda' at the top of their harsh, tuneless voices.

And I confess I was moved to tears when they came out to field, Davy lamps clanking from thick leather belts, miners' helmets jammed tightly on malformed heads, boots thumping and braces' buckles flashing.

In the evening, after the first day's play, they

politely declined our hospitality, preferring to dine off their own traditional native foods which, to my untutored eye, seemed to be composed entirely of boiled shirt tails and mouse droppings.

That night they slept under hedges, tightly wrapped in damp sacking, talking to themselves in their curious language which even to this day sounds to me like an obscure Madagascan accent being spoken backwards while suffering severely from an attack of piles.

Norman Riches scored 2 in the first innings and 175 in the second.

He is the first player I ever saw score a century while mounted on a pit pony.

Celia La Motta of Sussex Gardens
This is the Commodore's choice.

For some strange reason he is decidedly reticent in revealing his motives.

However, he assures me that she is a good sport and will pull her weight.

The Vileness comments that she'll probably pull everyone else's as well.

Damned if I know what he means.

S. J. McCabe of New South Wales and Australia
He was a small man, neat and dapper, who looked remarkably like that sweet little Matthew Engels of *The Manchester Guardian*, although he was a much superior writer.

He scored his runs with elegance and panache.

He had an abundance of guts, never better displayed than when he tamed Larwood, Voce and

Gubby Allen in his innings of 187 not out at Sydney in 1932.

He visited Witney Scrotum in 1936 and was bitten most fearsomely on the buttocks by the grounds-man's horse.

However, there are certain people in the village who claim that the culprit was the mother of the present Mrs Botham.

On this I am not qualified to comment.

I don't ever recall her biting my bottom.

Tungsten Forblatt of Racing Club de Trondheim CCC and Norway
Tungsten Forblatt enjoys the proud distinction of being the second lighthouse-keeper to represent Norway in international cricket.

He was a conscientious opening bat, a competent fielder in the deep and a sound medium pace bowler.

He once visited Witney Scrotum on a cycling holiday in 1938, but, finding a complete absence of lighthouses, departed almost immediately.

He bore a slight resemblance to Mr Edmundo Ros and always wore ginger Harris tweed hacking jackets.

In later life he opened the world's second indoor batting school north of the Arctic.

He was the sort of person who never comes first.

The All-Rounders:
G. H. Hirst of Yorkshire and England
I have in my possession an obituary of George Hirst, written by Wilfred Rhodes of immortal memory.

It reads thus:

'It seems strange when you lose an old pal like George Hirst.

'We have known each other for so long.

'Now that George has gone I am practically the only old-timer left.

'I shall miss him. He was one of the best – and the last of the old-timers.'

How moving.

How sad.

I think we'll take along Wilfred Rhodes, too, so they can keep each other company.

G. A. Faulkner of Transvaal and South Africa

During the course of a long and active life in which I have visited all four corners of the globe – and a few others as well – I have come to learn one indisputable, profound and deeply comforting philosophical notion – any man called Aubrey is automatically a 'good egg'.

Such was Aubrey Faulkner.

He was a stylish and handsome batsman and a bowler of the most fearsome googlies.

He was a man of grace, charm and wisdom.

He visited Witney Scrotum in the autumn of 1921, declaring that it was his intention to open up a dry cleaner's establishment.

Nothing ever came of it.

Damn pity – it's such a nuisance having to get the trusty Lanchester out to have my plus fours defrosted and dry cleaned at Keating New Town.

P. Taylor of Victoria and Australia

What a stirring story is his indeed.

Dragged out of obscurity to play against England

in the Sydney Test of '87 he damn near defeated England single-handed and was quite rightly nominated as man of the match.

I wonder if he's related to dear old Bob Taylor of Derbyshire and England, who was dragged out of the obscurity of the beer tent at Lord's to keep wicket for England in the summer of '86.

How I enjoyed his performance, though I can't help wishing he had had the grace to remove the bottle of Guinness from his hip pocket before taking up duty behind the stumps.

The wicketkeepers:
The Rev. M. M. Obsditch of Witney Scrotum
The Rev. Obsditch was the only man in the history of the 'summer game' to keep wicket while seated in an armchair.

Many people considered that Mr Gil Langley of South Australia and Australia had done so, concealing it inside the seat of his underpants. But this is not so.

A somewhat portly man with a bilious complexion and appalling table manners, the Rev. Obsditch first played for Witney Scrotum in 1839.

In that match he kept wicket immaculately while seated in an armchair and dining from a tray of cold pheasant, celery dumplings and vintage tawny port.

He played his last game in 1847, being forced to retire when he received a most painful blow in his castors.

R. T. Spooner of Warwickshire and England
He was the inspooner of the cricket ventorism.

He was an extremely fine kicketweeper.

The spinners:
Hok Pen Su of Shanghai Wanderers and China
He was undoubtedly the finest spin bowler ever produced by China – or indeed the whole of the Orient.

In his entire Test career he took one wicket.

He achieved cricketing immortality as the inventor of the most fiendish of deliveries, the 'Englishman'.

J. C. Laker of Surrey, Essex and England
Jim came to visit old Squire Brearley in Witney Scrotum shortly after his triumphant humiliation of the Australian scum at Old Trafford in 1956.

He was wearing elastic-sided brown boots.

A dear, dear man.

He is sadly missed by one and all.

D. L. A. Jephson of Cambridge University, Surrey and Witney Scrotum
It is maintained by historians of our beloved 'summer game' that Digby Loder Amroid Jephson's finest hour was when he took 6 for 21 bowling for the Gentlemen against the Players in 1898.

Among the batsmen he dismissed were Hayward, Storer, Brockwell, Albert Trott, Hirst and W. Mead – and that bowling lobs.

Now I am prepared to admit that that was an achievement of considerable proportions.

But can it compare with his deeds when he

moved to Witney Scrotum after he retired from the first-class game?

I think not.

And that's all I've got to say on the subject.

The fast bowlers:

R. Pollard of Lancashire and England

No man ever deserved more the title 'Richard the Lionheart'.

He is the choice of the Emaciated Vileness, Tinniswood, who insists I quote from the works of Denzil Batchelor, who he maintains is the finest and most neglected cricket writer of all time.

I agree.

Here is the relevant passage in all its glory:

'There are wicked and envious Southerners who wrote Dick Pollard off as a slinger. A very superior slinger, no doubt, but nothing over and above.

'These critics will find no widespread support for this opinion in any cobbled street where tripe and cow heel suppers are eaten on Saturday night to the music of Gracie Fields on the gramophone.

'From Westhoughton, his birthplace, to Wigan, Dick Pollard is regarded as the unluckiest good bowler since the season when simultaneously Hitler came to power and he made his debut in the first-class game.

'How often Pollard might have been chosen against Australia and wasn't. And look, urges Lancashire, what happened when he was.

'Didn't he force Bradman back on his wicket and get him plumb lbw in the Third Test Match in '48?

'You should have heard the roar that reverberated

round Old Trafford that sunlit July afternoon. Hampden Park never heard anything to surpass it.

'True they kept Dick Pollard in the side for one more match, when though he clean bowled Bradman he wasn't really successful.

'But they shouldn't have dropped him after that – and they should have called on him earlier and more often.

'With his heartwhole zest and sprawling, emphatic action he had sustained the Lancashire attack through thick and thin for many seasons.

'Eleven hundred and nineteen wickets in big cricket for 22 runs apiece!

'And there were ingrates at large (south of the Thames) who had moaned for years at the dearth of fast bowlers who could move the ball either way.

'Would you believe it?'

Indeed a bowler of the finest order and character.

And a writer sublime, witty and infinitely perceptive.

Both have been shamelessly neglected.

K. R. Miller of Victoria, New South Wales and Australia
He once danced with the lady wife at a Witney Scrotum Cricket Club hop in 1948.

His slow fox-trot was superb.

His tango was masterful.

His appeal against the lady wife in the ladies' invitation rhumba was most massive and monumental.

He was a bloody good cricketer, too.

R. R. Lindwall of New South Wales, Queensland and Australia.
Ray came to the hop, too, with his chum, Keith.

If memory serves me right, he danced very little.

He spent most of his time by the tea urn swapping yarns with the Commodore and whistling under his breath slightly out of tune.

Isn't it curious how things like that stick in the memory?

Wait a minute.

On second thoughts I think it was Ernie Toshack who came with Mr Miller.

A. C. Cordle of Glamorgan
Translator of Richard Strauss's 'Four Last Songs' into Welsh, Tony Cordle was the finest and most distinguished scholar-cricketer ever to have been produced by the Principality.

His Cubist paintings of Sofia Gardens are justifiably world-famous, and his murals on the walls of The Old Arcade public house in Cardiff have a delicacy and sensitivity unsurpassed in the history of the 'summer game'.

He once spent Christmas with us at Witney Scrotum and terrified the lady wife's loathsome Bedlington terriers.

Good man.

Well, there we are.

What a team, eh?

What a collection of characters.

Lovely, lovely cricket.

Next year we must compile a party of the all-time greats of ladies' netball.

6

Famous Sons

SPRING ADVANCED apace in Witney Scrotum.

Ten miles away in Keating New Town it was still midwinter. It always was.

But here in the village small birds sang besotted and bemused in tangled hedgerows.

Lapwings wheeled and whirled above Farmer Emburey's new-ploughed pastures.

Arctic-bound geese flew high above the sun-tossed Mendis Hills in great V-shaped straggles, and grass snakes and dry-lipped lizards sunned themselves on the sandy heathlands that skirted the vast and lonely Rumsey Downs.

And then one day the first house-martin of the summer arrived in Witney Scrotum and commenced to rebuild and refurbish its nest tucked in the eaves of the roof above the lady wife's bedroom.

The Brigadier stared long and hard at it as it sat

on the telephone wire twittering and preening itself with fastidious vagueness.

'Amazing, eh, Vileness?' he said. 'The poor little brute has travelled thousands and thousands of miles to get here. He's crossed vast deserts, towering mountain ranges, storm-tossed oceans to come back here to set up home outside the lady wife's bedroom.'

He paused for a moment, and then he said:

'Bloody fool. I wouldn't.'

Two collared doves cooed and bowed to each other from the top of a laurel tree, and rooks cawed and squabbled above their straggled nests high in the elms.

We began to walk slowly along the village street.

The sunshine was soft and benign, and it crooned to us.

Outside the Baxter Arms two of the village elders, Alston and Don 'Sir Oswald' Mosey dozed contentedly, great spirals of gnats billowing above the unbuttoned flies on their trousers.

The village idiot, old Ben Stansgate, was sitting happily in the village stocks munching greedily at a crumpled copy of *Labour Weekly*.

Mrs Botham had got herself a new spring hairdo, and the golden highlights and the pink and purple sequins flashed and sparkled.

We paused by the church, and the Brigadier said:

'Do you fancy a brisk turn round the graveyard?'

'Why not?' I said.

Curiously enough, in all my visits to Witney Scrotum I had never before visited the graveyard. It seemed an inappropriate thing to do when drunk.

The Brigadier led me through the rotting lychgate and over the thrusting, juicy grass, in which the last of the daffodils bent their withered heads to the timid breeze.

The headstones stood there, askew, tilting and crumbling, for all the world like spectators at the end of a Lancashire–Yorkshire match queueing on the platform of Warwick Road station.

We strolled among them, examining each inscription carefully.

I am bound to say it was a fascinating collection of names, among whom were:

W. G. Grace, Sir Horatio Mann – 'King of Cricket', Lord Hawke, C. B. Fry, John Nyren, Edgar Willsher, James Dark, Gracie Fields, Arthur Shrewsbury, Wilfred Rhodes, King Leopold of the Belgians, Nosmo King, J. Barton King, King Leopold of the Belgians, Stainless Stephen, Johnny Briggs, Bobby Peel, Sir Edward Elgar, W. Voce, Beethoven, King Leopold of the Belgians, Fred Archer, Grace Darling, Joe Darling, Victor Sylvester, Troise and some of his Mandoliers, An Unknown Wicket Keeper, Bing Crosby, Groucho Marx and King Leopold of the Belgians.

'I didn't know they were all buried here,' I said.

'They aren't,' said the Brigadier.

I raised my eyebrows.

'No need to do that,' said the Brigadier. 'It shows up the bloodshot in your piggy little eyes.'

I coughed and said:

'Well, why are they here?'

The Brigadier snorted impatiently and slapped the side of his plus fours with the blunt end of his stumper's mallet.

'I should have thought that was blindingly obvious,' he said.

'Is it?' I said, remembering just in time not to raise my eyebrows.

'Of course it is, you bloody fool,' said the Brigadier. 'It's Gooch, the blacksmith. He got a job lot of headstones from the Lord's Taverners Cruising Concert Party. Well, they died so many deaths on HMS *Canberra* that there weren't many of them left, so they let him have them at reduced rates. He'd nowhere to store them so he bunged them into the ground here. Then his wife gave him a monumental mason's gift kit for Christmas, so it was the natural thing to try it out here. I think he's doing King Leopold of the Belgians next.'

We passed by a headstone, on which was the inscription:

'Courtney Oates, Cricket Inventor. Born Witney Scrotum, 1800. Died (we think) 1885.'

The Brigadier patted it affectionately with his stumper's mallet.

'Now this one is really genuine,' he said.

'Really?' I said.

The Brigadier nodded and said:

'Let's sit on Queen Wilhelmina of the Netherlands, and I'll tell you all about him.'

We seated ourselves on the fallen headstone. A blackbird chackered. Wrens gurgled creamily. And the Brigadier launched into his story.

'Courtney Oates is probably one of the most famous sons ever to have been produced by Witney Scrotum.

'Forget Noël Coward and Bernard Braden –

Courtney Oates was one of the all-time greats, a village son to be proud of and cherish and celebrate.

'He was born under the most humble of circumstances.

'He was the illegitimate son of one Charlotte Oates, a junior stump polisher and matting wicket darner on the groundstaff of Squire Brearley.

'The father was unknown but was suspected to be either an itinerant philosopher of the School of Galileo's Experiential Dynamics or Higgs, the odd job man at the Cricket Bag Repository.

'On the discovery of her pregnancy she was instantly dismissed from the Squire's establishment. Homeless and distraught, she sought sanctuary in the stables of the hoof warehouse and thus six months later Courtney was born in a manger with swallows skudding low and blue above him and the groundsman's horse contentedly chomping at a discarded cricket pad, marinated in bat handle sauce.

'His physical appearance was somewhat unfortunate, his having been born bearing a marked resemblance to a completely toothless Mr Barry Wood, although there were those who maintained that his facial characteristics were somewhat similar to the feet of Miss Pam Shriver and the rear end of a Lancashire United tram car – an appearance which is all too familiar to me after a long and arduous marriage to the lady wife.

'Charlotte, however, was not to be gravelled by such misfortunes.

'She worshipped and adored the child.

'She scrimped and she scraped to bring up her son in conditions of the direst poverty and deprivation, an experience which many, many years later was to become only too familiar to Princess Michael of Kent.

'The young Courtney, despite all these handicaps, grew up to be a boy of considerable talent and promise.

'Under the tutelage of a penurious cricket writer and home hairdresser, Marlar, who sought sanctuary in the repository during the bitter winter of 1804, he learned how to read and write with such facility that by the age of seven he had already read the first sixteen volumes of the official biography of Sir Geoffrey Boycott and had sent seven letters in joined-up writing to Mr Barry Took, who at that time was editor of *Punch*, controller of BBC moving television and chairman of the Bank of England, his greatest years still to come.

'But it was with his hands that the young Courtney excelled.

'He was a born craftsman.

'He fashioned intricate models of threshing machines, dentists' waiting-rooms, chewing-gum dispensers and Mr Cliff Richard, who was yet to be transmogrified into Miss Mary O'Hara.

'From remaindered copies of Miss Jilly Cooper's *Me and My Barbour Coat* he built out of papier maché a fully-equipped en suite bathroom in crushed avocado for his mother, and for the Witney Scrotum Cricket Club he built a scorers' retiring room and salon privé out of wattle and pig dung – which might explain the subsequent anti-social behaviour of Mr Bill Frindall some several decades later during a summer heat wave.

'Yes, Courtney was a "natural".

'And so it was inevitable that at the age of nine he was apprenticed to the chief lift maintenance engineer at the hoof warehouse.

'His keenness and enthusiasm made a deep and lasting impression on one and all.

'Within a few weeks he had designed and constructed a completely new outside paternoster for the hoof warehouse guest annexe and indoor sports complex and built Witney Scrotum's first cable car system from the snug bar at the Baxter Arms to the new Pick N'Mix Bible Bookshop outside the Golf Ball Museum.

'And yet. . . .

'And yet what use had the great wide world outside the confines of the village for these inventions?

'Who could find suitable employ for the hover-mowers and rowing machines he built in the back garden of old Grannie Swanton's cottage? What demand was there for stapling machines and light-weight office furniture in those early days of the nineteenth century?

'No, it seemed that he was destined to lead out a life of total obscurity and the direst of poverty.

'And then came his "big chance".

'It was given to him by the wife of Squire Brearley.

'The circumstances were thus:

'For three years Squire Brearley, a somewhat short-sighted person of gentle mien and stubborn nature, had been opening the batting for Witney Scrotum despite all advice to the contrary.

'Though of an excessively elderly, nay doddery and wizened appearance and habit – much as his more famous descendant displayed many years later when captaining England – he was still a man in his prime well able to cope with the nuptial desires and responsibilities concentrated in the nether regions of the popping crease.

'However, such was the fallibility of his eyesight and the ferocity of the opposing fast bowlers that in each innings he played he was struck at least five violent blows in what can only be decently described as his "privates", which after the subsequent enlargement of same astute onlookers and observers of the medical scene were to dub his "lieutenant colonels".

'His wife, a handsome, vigorous woman with large equine teeth and prominent shin bones, was much distressed by her husband's inability to fulfil the obligations of the matrimonial nocturnal container and finally "put her foot down".

' "Ranulph," she said. 'It is three years since I last had an innings with you. I feel like the second wicketkeeper on an MCC tour to Australia – frustrated, unwanted and only of use as a servant during drinks intervals. Therefore, unless you take steps to protect yourself and your intimates during this coming season, I shall be compelled to find a new opening partner.'

'The Squire was mortified.

'He did not know what to do.

'He could not let the team down, and yet he was reluctant to go down to number three in the order with his wife.

'The first match of the season came up, and in a panic he took the first thing at hand to use as a protector.

'As luck would have it, it happened to be the family's pet tortoise.

'The Squire was rather pleased with his ingenuity.

'Little did he realise as he stuffed the reptile down the front of his trousers as he prepared to go out to bat that the creature had long since ceased its hibernation.

'And thus his downfall.

'And thus Courtney's rise to fame and fortune.

'It was a dazzlingly blue morning in early summer as Squire Brearley walked out on to the sward to open the innings with the ancestor of the present Gooch, the village blacksmith.

'He faced up to the first ball with not a little trepidation.

'As usual the opposing bowler was a giant of a man with bristling black moustaches, ruddy face, narrow eyes, bulging sinews and a backside as large as two bags of cement.

'As usual the first ball he received struck him the most thunderous blow in the privates.

'To his joy he felt no pain.

'To his unbounded relief he felt no hint of discomfort.

'A great grin of happiness spread over his benign and innocent features.

'And then disaster struck.

'The tortoise, which had been dozing peacefully, absent-mindedly munching a piece of lettuce left over from the previous season in the Squire's trousers, was most rudely disturbed and alarmed by the blow which had struck his shell.

'Accordingly he poked out his head.

'In the darkness inside the crutch of the Squire's trousers he could see nothing.

'He blinked hard.

'And then a chink of light appeared.

'He extended his head slowly forwards and thrust his head out through the source of light.

'It was the gap between the third and fourth button of the Squire's flies.

'He blinked in the sunlight.

'He turned his head to the right.

'He turned his head to the left.

'He slowly raised it up and down.

'The fielders and spectators looked on in horror.

'Two spinster ladies from Cirencester visiting distant cousins in the village fainted on the spot.

'The umpire at the bowler's end turned fifteen shades of puce and rattled the coins in his pocket most ferociously.

'And thus was the Squire the first and only man in the history of our beloved "summer game" to be given out: "Hit wicket – indecent exposure".

'The humiliation and mockery he suffered subsequently were of such strength and constancy that he resolved there and then never to play cricket again.

' "Nonsense, Ranulph," said his wife as they lay side by side in bed later that night. "At long long last we have shared a fruitful and profitable opening partnership and you have managed to carry your bat throughout the innings. Of course you shall play cricket again and you shall also be fit to fulfil your conjugal responsibilities. Leave it to me.'

'Accordingly next morning she presented herself at the hoof warehouse and said in an imperious voice:

' "Oates, I wish you to make me an abominable protector."

'Courtney looked at her with bewilderment.

'You what, ma'am?' he said.

' "I wish you to make me an abominable protector for the Squire," she said. 'And I wish it to be portable, too."

'Courtney shook his head. Despite his skill as an inventor he was still an innocent youth, unworldly in the ways of net practice and mutual nude splogging in the bath. He was deeply puzzled.

' "And what might an abominable protector be, ma'am?" he said.

'The Squire's wife tapped her feet impatiently.

' "It's a device to protect his thingies," she said.

' "His what, ma'am?" said Courtney, scratching his head.

' "His do-dahs. You know."

' "I don't ma'am. That I do not."

'The Squire's wife clicked her tongue and breathed heavily down flared nostrils.

' "Oates," she said. "I realise you are a young man who has never set foot outside this village. I realise you are not well-versed in the niceties and complexities of the relationships between man and woman. I realise you are shy and confused. I shall, therefore, put it to you as delicately as I possibly can. I want you to invent a device that will prevent my husband from being constantly hit in the pills."

' "Ah, now I understands," said Courtney, a great beam spreading over his face. "What you wants is something to protect his nadgers so you can have your bit of nookie on Saturday nights."

'The Squire's wife nodded.

' "Right then, ma'am," said Courtney. "And what size would you be requiring?"

'The squire's wife flushed slightly on the neck and lowered her eyelids.

'Tentatively and slowly she cupped her hands and hesitantly extended her arms.

' "Well, from memory," she said. "It would be about that size."

'Courtney beamed once more.

' "Right, ma'm," he said. "It shall be done. And if I gets into difficulties I shall examine the groundsman's horse and compare notes."

'And so for three long months Courtney laboured long and hard.

'During this time great showers of sparks billowed from his furnace. Monstrous clanking and whirring noises clattered from his workshop. Malodorous clouds of dense black smoke belched from the tall, gaunt chimneys of the hoof warehouse.

'At the end of this period Courtney had fashioned an implement which was to revolutionise not only the world of cricket but the whole sphere of human activities beyond the confines of the most precious of beloved summer games.

'At this stage it was rather crude in design, consisting of three sheets of heavily tarred ship's canvas stretched across a frame of cast iron and clamped into place with horseshoes bound tightly together with triple-strand barbed wire.

'It proved slightly cumbersome to wear.

'The Squire had to be transported to the wicket on the back of the groundsman's horse and held upright by four of the stoutest lads from the village John Player tug-of-war team.

'But, by God, it worked.

'The first ball he received passed clean through the gap between bat and pad and hit him flush on the abominable protector.

'He felt not the slightest pain.

'The subsequent clang, however, deafened fieldsman and spectator alike and was clearly heard on the opposite side of the Bristol Channel, by the simple souls inhabiting Lundy Island, and caused Mr Tony Lewis in Neath to spill his cornflakes all over yet another of his begging letters to become Lord Henry Blofeld's pencil sharpening wallah on the BBC ball-by-ball commentary team.

'But what an impact it made on the "summer game".

'Its fame spread far and wide like a bushfire.

'Orders poured into Courtney at the hoof warehouse.

'Soon he was working night and day producing his abominable protectors for cricketers the length and breadth of the country, most of which orders came from their wives, sweethearts and live-in spinster retired Royal Naval stokers.

'Very soon the hoof warehouse became too small for his activities and he was compelled to establish premises in the building which was later to become the village Do It Yourself Planetarium.

'The entire work force of Witney Scrotum was drafted in to keep up with the demand.

'Courtney himself was forced to give up the workbench and repair to his study where he spent month after month refining his invention until soon he had received orders from all the royal heads of Europe who found its use most efficacious in the employ of armoured gun turrets for the dreadnoughts of their respective navies.

'The president of the United States of America ordered a dozen to be kept in bond for utilisation as facial lift-off facilities to a future Nancy Reagan.

'The grandfather of the present Miss Beryl Bainbridge ordered one, which she has used most successfully as make-up on her recent moving television programmes.

'And in the course of time the appliance was so refined that it is now used the world over as a winter chest protector for the divine Miss Sue Lawley and a money belt for discredited directors of the Guinness Stout and Insider Swiss Roll Company PLC.

'What could be more natural, therefore, than that after this outstanding success Courtney should turn his hand to other inventions of a cricketing bent.

'Here in Witney Scrotum he produced the world's first waterproof and inflammable sightscreen.

'He created the David Constant armoured Panama hat and the Richie Benaud reversible mouth.

'He invented the Ian Botham luminous hair net and musical Carmen rollers.

'With his own two hands he made the world's first manifestation of Mr Gordon Garlick of Lancashire and Northamptonshire.

'Small wonder that with such great successes he should reluctantly leave his native heath and seek pastures new to extend and develop the full flowering of his talents.

'He wandered the world and in the fullness of time achieved international immortality with the munificence and ingenuity of his inventions and creations, among which were the design and building of the Bramall Lane pavilion, the establishment of the international dialling code for the talking telephone, the discovery of the autocycle chain guard and the introduction of anti-fungal foot powder to the dressing-room of Yorkshire County Cricket Club.

'Having thus achieved fame and fortune, he returned in his declining years to Witney Scrotum.

'There he lived out the rest of his life making fretwork models of Anton Bruckner, Two Ton Tony Galento and King Leopold of the Belgians.

'He met his Maker a vaguely happy man.

'And to this day the simple folk of Witney Scrotum are convinced he was the first man to have invented death – or, in its other manifestation, a cricket commentary by Mr Tony Lewis.'

7
Another Bloody Wife

SUMMER BURST the flood banks of spring and deluged Witney Scrotum with its creamy white waves of elder and its gurgling torrents of song from blackbird and chiff-chaff.

Nearer and nearer came the day of the visit of the Australians to celebrate the proud and momentous day of the bicentenary of the village cricket club.

Buzzards mewed high above the hanging oak woods, cattle lowed juicily in the fat-bellied dusks, Shire horses, fetlock-deep in buttercupped pastures, thumped their hooves in frisk-tailed abandon.

Brown trout waxed fat and languid in the sun-sparked waters of the River Buse.

At long, long last Don 'Sir Oswald' Mosey had received his £5 winter heating allowance from the

Ink Monitor at Number Ten and the village had welcomed with open arms its new district chiropodist and Tupperware counsellor in the shape of Mary 'Poppins' Parkinson.

It was rumoured that the village idiot, old Ben Stansgate, was to appear on *Desert Island Discs*.

And then came the bombshell.

I had my first intimations of the disaster when the Brigadier burst into the attic high at the top of his residence, kicked the rear legs of the camp bed, on which I was sleeping, spinning me unceremoniously to the floor and bellowed:

'Vileness, the worst possible has occurred.'

I massaged my bruised limbs, reassembled myself within my pyjama trousers and said:

'And what is that?'

The Brigadier held up a letter and waved it high above his head.

'This,' he said. 'This. I have been mortally deceived and treacherously betrayed.'

In vain did I attempt to comfort him.

In vain did I pour copious draughts of bunion plaster Bacardi from my hip flask down his gullet.

In vain did I softly massage his stumper's mallet and debase myself before his Thermogene-lagged plus fours.

Tears cascaded down his cheeks.

His shoulders heaved.

His ears twirled.

I waited, silent and solicitous.

The spotted flycatcher rasped the ivy on the walls outside my window.

A distant milk float rattled, a cock crowed thrice, and faintly from far below in the house came the voice of Mr Jimmy Young interviewing a representative from Age Concern.

At length the Brigadier held up the letter once more and said in a weak, tear-choked voice:

'It's from Mr P. H. Edmunds of Middlesex and England. He can't come to our great day.'

I paused for a moment and then I said gently:

'Tell me. Tell me all about it.'

The Brigadier snuffled long and phlegmingly into his I Zingari handkerchief and then commenced the following discourse:

'Poor Philippe Henri.

'Poor, sad, benighted booby.

'Fancy being married to "that woman".

'The horror of it. The unrelieved ghastliness of that endless self-opinionated chatter ringing in his ears as he desperately tries to write his leader articles for the *Financial Times*, or seeks solace in the ablutions office listening to Morning Service on the BBC World Service, trousers round his ankles, in the wee small hours.

'No wonder his bald patch grows larger and larger.

'No wonder his wrist bands grow limper and limper.

'No wonder he has finally abandoned his life's work in trying to restore the monarchy to Bulgaria in the person of Mr Mike Brearley.

'Do you know, Vileness, when the truth about the wretchedness of his marriage was revealed to a stunned nation, he was engulfed by great tidal waves of sympathy and compassion.

'*The Week's Good Cause* on the talking wireless, done most movingly on his behalf by Sir Pelham

Warner and Mr Douglas Jardine, drew one of the most generous responses ever experienced by that most noble of programmes.

'Within an hour of the broadcast, donations were received from Shelter, Age Concern, Oxfam and Mr Tim Brooke-Taylor who can't bear to be left out of anything.

'Senior citizens huddled over evil-smelling paraffin stoves in dank and damp garrets in the fetid slums of Glasgow and the arid wastelands of Liverpool dug deep into their threadbare pockets to send half-sucked cough lozenges and defunct bus passes to the appeal.

'Mr E. W. "Gloria" Swanton donated his entire collection of the records of Billy J. Kramer and the Dakotas to the fund.

'And Sir Geoffrey Boycott, brooding in the vastness of his great Yorkshire estates, sent a message to the nation intimating that in time he would send a substantial cheque to the cause provided he could find a new nib for his fountain pen.

'Yes, I know all this, Vileness.

'I appreciate the generosity of spirit which has provoked this amazing outburst of sympathy and united these "sceptred isles" of ours in a way not experienced since those ghastly, desperate days of starvation, deprivation and misery before the Ink Monitor took up her reign at Downing Street and in an instant restored self-respect and patriotic pride by appointing Princess Peter May of Teck as chairman of selectors.

'Yes, yes, I know all this.

'But I have to "come clean".

'I have to tell you, Vileness, that I feel not one jot of pity for poor Philippe Henri Edmunds.

'He has brought all this calamity on himself.

'It is his responsibility and his alone.

'He never should have married "that woman".

'It was simply asking for trouble tying the matrimonial knot with Princess Michael of Kent.

'Have you ever seen her on the moving television? – a typical Hun for all the world to see, hectoring, barking at us in those clipped, malformed vowels as she desperately tries to master the basic principles of the English language, grousing and grumbling, flashing her protruding teeth, as she holds up a never-ending collection of phallic carrots sent to her by mentally-retarded viewers or accosting bemused Japanese tourists outside Harrods, inviting them to blow bubbles of bath foam out of their navels.

'I cannot abide her, and neither can that nice Mr Desmond Wilcox, who once passed through Witney Scrotum on a bicycling holiday in the company of the Princess Royal, who I must confess sat rather uneasily in his saddle bag.

'I am not a prejudiced man, but in my day first-class county cricketers did not concern themselves with matters like marriage, child-bearing and nocturnal activities in the environs of the popping crease.

'They were chaste in word, deed and thought.

'They abhorred strong drink, foul language and forward women with Welsh accents and sharp teeth, and never in their wildest imagination would they have dreamed of having "carnal relations" with members of the opposite sex of a non-cricketing bent.

'To my certain knowledge this code of conduct obtains to this very day.

'I can, therefore, only assume that Philippe Henri must have had nothing less than a brainstorm when he decided to "throw in his lot" with this revolting woman who spends all her waking hours clambering in and out of helicopters on the moving television exposing her over-large posterior to first-class umpires and county cricket scorers who simply do not have the worldly experience or moral fibre to cope with exhibitionism of such a provocative nature.

'I must now declare my interest in this matter, Vileness.

'For reasons of a deeply personal nature I have long kept secret the fact that Philippe Henri (or "Embers", as he is known to his colleagues in the Middlesex County Cricket Club) was in fact nurtured, nourished and educated in the use of cake fork and abacus by no less than the lady wife and myself here in our precious village of Witney Scrotum.

'Would that I could have said the name of Mr Roy Hattersley or Miss Dorothy Tutin.

'But fate was not to grant us such solace in our declining years.

'Instead it drafted into our care the small, sickly innocent child, who, despite all our loving care and attention, was in later life to bring upon us shame and ignominy by appearing on the talking wireless on *Start the Week* with the odious Dame Richard Baker, being constantly interrupted and contradicted by his wife, who would have been much better employed fulfilling her self-imposed mission in life – preparing Mr Billy Connolly to take his place in high society as crib partner to the Duchess of Kent.

'We can no longer bear the shame.

'Now at the time of the bicentenary of Witney Scrotum Cricket Club it must come out now before others for reasons best known to themselves decide to expose "the wrong side of the coin".

'I say this because in recent weeks I have seen, lurking in the lee of the Cricket Bag Repository, a revolting, snuff-stained creature looking remarkably like Mr Chapman Snitcher of the *Daily Express*.

'While I am prepared to accept his story that the secretary to the cabinet, Mr Warwick Armstrong, has been a long-time agent of the KGB, I do not wish to be burdened by the public opprobrium of his assertions that I was in some way responsible for inflicting "that woman" on my fellow countrymen.

'So here, Vileness, is the "true story".

'The lady wife and I first came across Philippe Henri when we were visiting missionaries and lacrosse coaches in the more remote parts of Northern South West British Dexterland (or, as it was then called, Zambia).

'We were inspecting an isolated Barbour coat plantation "somewhere up country" when the lady wife found floating in a moses basket in a stagnant irrigation ditch a small child.

'It was wrapped in swaddling clothes and Okapi skin nappies.

'It had obviously been "well tended" and "well loved".

'It had attached to its neck a label on which was written:

' "Forgive me, but I just cannot cope – Kenneth Kaunda."

'The lady wife insisted that we should take the infant home, averring that it would be good company for her Bedlington terriers.

'Despite my avid protestations she secreted the creature in the depths of my portable cricket bag in order to avoid quarantine regulations on our return to Blighty.

'And thus on a day of tepid spring sunshine, intermittent showers and "slow play" at Buxton, Derbyshire versus Leicestershire, we introduced Philippe Henri to the bosom of our hearth here in Witney Scrotum.

'Why call him Philippe Henri, I hear you ask.

'Well, the lady wife insisted that he had a typical French appearance, looking at that tender age remarkably like a half-chewed breakfast croissant.

'Accordingly, she christened him Philippe after Louis Philippe Joseph de Bourbon-Orléans, whose face she had once seen on a W. D. and H. O. Wills cigarette card.

'And Henri after the celebrated lawn tennis player, Henri Cochet, whom she had once seen buying a toilet roll in a "well-known" department store in Knightsbridge.

'I asked her circumspectly why she had, therefore, not christened the infant Harvey Nicholls Izal, but she simply snorted and flashed her piggy little eyes.

'Philippe Henri settled in instantly.

'He responded well to his diet of rusks and Winalot and was soon able to fetch my slippers with "the best of them", although I am bound to say he developed an annoying habit of burying his Meccano set in the lady wife's edible vegetable patch.

'We kept his presence a strictly guarded secret from our fellow villagers.

'As soon as he had come through his fifth moult we locked him in the boot of the trusty Lanchester and took him to a prep school in the heart of rural Wales recommended to us in the columns of *The Cricketer* as an establishment where small boys would be taught the rudiments of good table manners, polite speech and dextrous fielding in the leg trap. It was, I believe, the alma mater of Mr Tony Lewis, who in later life was to achieve even wilder fame as Mr Tony Lewis.

'I fear things did not go well for our young charge.

'The diet of cold laver bread and boiled cricket balls was not to his liking and on visiting him for the first time five years later we discovered that the little black boy we had found abandoned in the hinterlands of Central Africa had turned into a small, wizened, white creature with fair hair, pink eyelids and the curious lilting Latvian accent he has maintained to this very day.

'Bang, of an instant, went my plans for being the personal manager of the new Harry Belafonte.

'We resolved to withdraw him from school immediately.

'But where to take him?

'It was the lady wife who "came up" with the answer.

'He would be quartered with her unmarried spinster sister in Cheltenham and there his education would "take its proper course".

'The enterprise was an outstanding success.

'Within three years the shy, timid, painfully inarticulate little boy we had thrown out of the back seat of the trusty Lanchester concealed in a British Home Stores carrier bag had turned into a strapping blonde Adonis of bristling young manhood, self-confident, assertive, with a deep, knowing twinkle to his eye.

'I maintain it was his education at the Cheltenham Ladies' College which had "done the trick".

'The lady wife, however, preferred the theory that the spectacular change had been prompted by constant exposure to her unmarried spinster sister's rigorous regime of cold, early-morning baths in unfermented Adidas, stewed prunes in Gregory powder sauce and nude pole vaulting.

'Be that as it may, the fact remains that he passed all his examinations with the utmost aplomb and distinction and, after serving as a general in the King's Own African Rifles, went up to Cambridge University, where a glittering future awaited him in his chosen field of studies of Classical Studies and Home Dressmaking.

'He seemed destined for "great things", and the lady wife and I had high hopes that in the fullness of time he would take up his rightful place as Professor of Double Glazing at the Open University.

'At first all went well.

'The life of "the dreaming spires" suited him to perfection.

'He grew into a sophisticated, debonair young man, who yet retained a natural charm which manifested itself in his fondness for forensic science, the lesser known string quartets of Zoltan Kodaly and his friendship with Mr Jonathan 'Dusty' Miller, who was later to put in such yeoman service with Derbyshire County Cricket Club.

'He had a natural sporting prowess, too.

'He gained quarter Blues in rounders and spelling bees, and to my great delight excelled at our beloved "summer game".

'Good God, I remember thinking, if he continues in this vein, he might yet become another Mr Ramon Subba Row. But then common sense prevailed, and I realised that the most I could hope for was that he became a second Mr Eric Bedser – with all that entailed.

'The lady wife, of course, preened herself with pleasure at the success of her protégé, and after much mutual discussion of a one-sided nature she prevailed upon me to invite him back to our village and expose him to public view.

'We presented him to our fellow villagers quite openly and without a shred of shame as the distant nephew of a remote cousin who had fallen upon hard times in his School for Abseiling in Bangladesh.

'Philippe Henri was an instant success.

'Miss Roebuck from the dog biscuit shop turned scarlet to her collar bones every time he passed by her window and every morning sent him round gifts of millet sprays and cuttle fish bones tied in pink satin bows.

'He spent long hours in the back room of the Baxter Arms quaffing vast quantities of untreated scrumpy overflow with Farmer Emburey, Prodger the poacher and Don "Sir Oswald" Mosey.

'Every afternoon he would trip gaily to old Squire Brearley's and there in the cool depths of his study, lined with its team photographs of Darlington FC and Rochdale Hornets, he would patiently paint in the old man's Wittgenstein colouring books for him, clip his toenails and take out the spelling mistakes in his articles for *The Sunday Times*.

'And then to our great joy in the Christmas vacation of his last year at Varsity he brought home to us his "young lady".

'What a delightful creature she was.

'I think her name was Frances – but I can't be sure. Christian names of members of the opposite sex were never my strong point. I sometimes think that's why I must have married the lady wife.

'Anyway, Philippe Henri told us that he had met her in a quiet bookshop in Cambridge surreptitiously secreting a volume of the works of Matthew Engels into the hood of her special *Observer* offer Lapland anorak.

'She had stood there frozen with fear.

'He had smiled at her understandingly, squeezed her right arm gently and said:

' "Don't worry, my dear. I shall not tell the authorities. Allow me to purchase the book for you and thereafter let us repair to a quiet tea room I know which serves the most delicious custard creams and draught Tizer."

' "Gosh," she exclaimed. "You speak Afrikaans."

'And thus their love sprouted, prospered and bloomed.

'Philippe Henri, of course, "made all the running".

'She had no friends at Varsity, and he introduced her to his friends in the Rover Scouts, the Cyclists' Touring Club and the Interdenominational Stamp Collecting Society.

'They shared a common interest in plain, wholesome food and early nights, and in "next to no time" he felt emboldened to invite her to spend her Christmas hols here with us in Witney Scrotum.

'The lady wife took an immediate shine to her.

'She was gawky, painfully shy, flat-chested and spoke only when spoken to – and that in a hesitant, soft whisper that scarcely ruffled the tassles on her special *Observer* Patagonian poncho.

'She had an innate, shining modesty, blotchy elbows, insipid ankles, and she looked at one coyly out of the tops of her eyes rather like dear Princess Diana did before she became the Countess Spencer.

'The lady wife resolved that they should marry.

'An outgoing, charming, suave, somewhat irresponsible young man like Philippe Henri needed a mousey little wife to keep him on "an even keel", she argued. And she could see it all:

'He would return from his job in the city or in

123

the Difficult Sums department at Varsity or playing for England against Sri Lanka, and she would be waiting for him, compliant, passive and attentive to his every whim.

'On those "special" nights she would have cooked a cottage pie for him and they would watch *Play Your Cards Right* on the moving television.

'Immersed in the loving intimacy of their own company they would need no friends to intrude upon their sessions of Trivial Pursuit or to share their early suppers of wholemeal cream crackers and caffeine-free coffee.

'They would be frugal in the nuptial bed and never send their sheets to the laundry after congress.

'They would keep a joint scrapbook and Philippe Henri would buy a fretwork machine and make Swiss cuckoo clocks and pipe racks as Christmas presents for his colleagues in the England cricket team.

'The lady wife did not mention her dreams to the young lovers, of course, but as she saw them driven away from our front door in the Commodore's bottle green Humber with its Rhode Island reds dangling from the front bumper and the gardener desperately trying to disentangle his bicycle clips from the rear mudguard, she said to me:

' "All will be well. You'll see. You'll see."

'It was not.

'That was the last time we ever clapped eyes on Philippe Henri and his young lady "in the flesh".

'What had we done to them?

'What perfidies had we committed in our innocence to deserve such wanton cruelty?

'Surely to goodness I could be forgiven for having unwittingly disturbed the young lady in the ablutions offices darning a hole in her special *Observer* offer Swiss Army thermal knickers?

'I fear I shall never know. For ten long years we heard nothing from Philippe Henri.

'Oh yes, I read about him in the newspapers, both quality and the *Daily Telegraph*.

'I heard his name frequently mispronounced on the ball-by-ball Test Match Special commentary by Mr Frederick Trueman.

'But I found it too painful to watch him on the moving television, having his every movement intimately analysed by Mr Richie Benaud and his mouth.

'And then quite suddenly he appeared on our screens one evening after our local news programme had featured an outbreak of swine fever in Keating New Town and the "hot" results of our Auxiliary Fire Brigade summer raffle.

'And he was with "that woman".

'And she was jumping up and down on her seat.

'And she was shouting and gesticulating and shaking him by the arm and butting in every time he attempted to speak.

'And on his face was that dear little bewildered smile we had first seen on the face of the tiny black mite we had whisked from the depths of the Marks and Spencer moses basket all those years ago.

'My heart turned over.

'I began to weep softly to myself.

'I had no heart for working the points on the Commodore's electric train set that evening.

'I had no enthusiasm for sprinkling itching powder in the basket of the lady wife's loathsome Bedlington terriers.

'That, Vileness, was last night.

'And then this morning I received quite out of the blue a letter.

'The letter bore the distinctive hand of Philippe Henri. And it was in real writing, too.

'I ripped it open, and on the cheap hotel note-paper I read the following.

My dear Brigadier,

I was about to spring a surprise on you.

It was my intention to visit you, quite unan-nounced, on the day of the bicentenary of the Witney Scrotum Cricket Club.

But I am afraid events have caught up with me.

Oh, my God, how they have indeed.

Another bloody tour.

I only went to the West Indies so she could write another one of her bloody smart-arsed books.

And now I'm on another tour – Sheffield, Birmingham, Leeds, Manchester, Glasgow, Edinburgh. It's only because of her. Honestly, if I go to another book-signing or TV chat show, I swear I shall scream. If I sit in the control box of another local radio station, I shall do my nut.

What have I done to deserve this? What have I . . .

No.

Keep calm. Keep calm, my son. Last night the Marquesa and I had lobster for supper. Lobster is a shellfish that is boiled alive in its shell and can be served either with a garnish of tangy cheese, bacon and bechamel sauce, or *au naturel* with fresh country herbs.

Au naturel means it hasn't been messed about with.

Oh God, I'm *in extremis*.

In extremis means . . .

Christ, I must stop explaining everything I write.

I must stop . . .

I must stop it all. Everything. All I ever wanted out of life was to be a cricketer and go on tour with the chaps and make apple pie beds for Ian Botham and throw people into swimming pools and creep up behind them silently and shout Boo just as they are about to drink their rum punch.

That's not much to ask from a graduate of Cambridge University, is it?

And now what have I ended up with?

I'd set my heart on coming to your bicentenary match.

I've been looking forward to it for ages and ages.

And now what's happened?

That woman has . . .

'The rest of the letter was obscured with a savage criss-crossing of blue felt pen, and on the side of the margin was the impression of a large rubber

127

stamp bearing the word "Censored" and obviously done by the hand of a woman.

'Well, all I can say, Vileness, is that I have not the slightest sympathy for Philippe Henri.

'Any man who has the lack of foresight to marry a woman who sails single-handed across the Atlantic, reads the news on moving television with long, dangling earrings, becomes a Junior Minister of Health, and writes books on Hollywood wives deserves all he gets.'

8

The Half Century

NEARER AND NEARER came the great day.

The sun blistered Witney Scrotum.

It battered the village.

It scorched the meadows. It dried up water-courses. It melted the iron stays on old Grannie Swanton's herbal corsets.

PC Jesty's truncheon went down with sunstroke. Old Squire Brearley's beard caught fire spontaneously as he was opening a tin of Bisto and he had to be taken by tractor to Keating New Town to be put out. Mrs Botham's new hair-do was severely cut back by an outbreak of barley weevil and maize hip.

Yet all the time the villagers laboured long and cheerfully on their preparations for the most memorable day in their history.

The cricket pitch was shaved and watered daily

and guarded at night by volunteers against the possible depredations of escaped budgerigars and wandering locusts.

The cesspit at the rear of the cricket pavilion urinals was emptied and its contents used in Farmer Emburey's special bicentenary extra vintage scrumpy.

And Miss Roebuck from the dog biscuit shop had laboured night and day for eight months embroidering an exquisite sampler and tapestry depicting scenes in the history of Witney Scrotum.

It now hung in the tap room of the Baxter Arms, being used as a tea towel and on Saturday nights as a combined bib for the village elders, Alston and Don 'Sir Oswald' Mosey.

And in the middle of it all I suddenly realised this:

By a curious, delightful and wholly felicitous coincidence I was to attain my half century during the very year that Witney Scrotum Cricket Club celebrated two hundred years of its existence.

Fifty years old!

Good God, I was almost as old as Raymond Illingworth when he made his first appearance for Yorkshire Colts.

Fifty years old!

What had been happening to this great country in the year of my birth?

Who was opening the innings for Worcestershire?

What was the name of the Leicestershire scorer?

Had Edmundo Ros already written those immortal lines:

I lisped in rhumbas,
Because the rhumbas came.

Fifty years old! My half century!
I raised my bat – but not for long.

My wife and I celebrated my birthday by eating a packed luncheon of sardines, soda bread and Mr Kipling Breakwell tarts in the dentistry section of Foyle's Book Shop in Charing Cross Road.

Never in the whole of my life had I seen so many bad fillings – and that includes the contents of the sandwiches.

Fifty years old!

Friends, shopkeepers and Minor Counties umpires of nodding acquaintance have asked me if I feel any great changes in the quality of my life now that I have attained the span of two score and ten – or to be more precise the exact total minus two made by Mr Graham Atkinson in the second innings, Somerset versus Essex, Taunton, 3 May 1962.

I am bound to say that I do.

The differences between the ages of forty-nine and fifty are spectacular.

I have suddenly noticed an alarming tendency to butt in when Mr Clay Jones is delivering his words of wisdom during *Gardeners' Question Time*.

More alarming, I find myself trying to harmonise in the treble clef during *Songs of Praise* on BBC Sunday night television and attempting to find the answers to puzzles set by Mr Bruce Forsyth on *Play Your Cards Right*.

Old age is indeed a cruel affliction to bear.

And then, even worse, I think of my beloved African grey parrot.

He is four.

Dear Lord, by the time I am long since gone and buried beneath the hawthorns at the Taff End of Sofia Gardens, he will still be a young bird in his prime with a life expectancy of many years ahead – it is remotely possible that he could still be alive the year Yorkshire rebels restore Sir Geoffrey Boycott to the captaincy of their county.

To whom shall I bequeath him?

No problem.

I shall leave him to the authorities at Lord's with the specific request that he be stationed in his cage in the Long Room, where he can spend his declining years screeching at the top of his voice those immortal words:

'Sod Norman Gifford.'

He is already an accomplished impersonator of Princess Peter May of Teck, and his repertoire of the more esoteric vowel movements of Mr Trevor Bailey is extensive, so there can be little doubt that he would be an invaluable asset to the memorabilia of 'headquarters' – almost as exciting as the permanent exhibition of Mr Norman Cowans' pubic hairs.

It was with such notions of the deepest philosophical nature ringing through my sun-parched beard that I returned once more to Witney Scrotum.

I was greeted by the Brigadier, who was in a state of the highest excitement.

'Whatho, Vileness,' he said. 'I have two items of the most vital of import to pass on to you.'

'Oh yes?' I said, desperately trying to conceal a yawn in the sleeve of my wife's birthday present of a Marks and Spencer Taiwanese leisure sweater and auxiliary table cloth.

'Yes,' said the Brigadier. 'First of all I have discovered the christian names of Miss Roebuck from the dog biscuit shop.'

In an instant every nerve and fibre of my body was intense and vibrant.

Crikey, one of the greatest mysteries of our beloved 'summer game' was about to be revealed.

All my basest instincts as a hack journalist and contributor to the *Radio Times* and *Cheshire Life* jostled for attention.

Where was the nearest telephone?

Was there a telex machine in the porter's rest room and conservatory at Graveney Junction?

With information of this sort I could clean up with both front page and back page of the *Sun* newspaper and establish myself as a columnist *sine die* (and unpaid) on *The Independent*.

Miss Roebuck's christian names!

'What are they?' I gasped. 'For Glory's sake, tell me her christian names.'

The Brigadier smiled.

And then he said very slowly and very deliberately:

'Nyree Dawn.'

I fainted on the spot.

Nyree Dawn Roebuck.

Now it all fitted into place.

Those flushes over Colin Dredge. The constant swooning at the mention of the name of Soames De Freitas. The sad, homesick-riddled correspondence with the *Sunday Times* from Australia.

Now I understood the reason for the signed

picture of Eric Porter pinned on the front of her hamster and gerbil salon.

Before I could ponder more over this most wicked snippet of information the Brigadier delivered his other item of news.

'Vileness,' he said. 'I have been invited to deliver a speech at a luncheon of the Lord's Taverners.'

Of an instant I fainted once more.

A speech to the Lord's Taverners – could any greater accolade and honour be awarded to a citizen of our noble and sceptred isles?

I instantly thought back to those who had received similar summons to glory – Mr Tim Brooke-Taylor, Mr Bill Tidy, Doctor Frederick Sewards Trueman, Professor of Dropped 'Aitches and Difficult Sums at the University of Bramall Lane, Princess Michael of the Huns, King Zof of Albania and Derbyshire County Cricket Club, Mr Andrew Lloyd-Webster and his delicious songstress wife, Miss Marti Webb, Lord Mountbatman, Mrs Gerald Legge, Lady Lewisham, Viscountess Dartmouth, Countess Spencer and her husband, Terry, Mr Richard Hutton and his son, Sir Leonard, and, of course, Miss Miriam Margolis, impersonating the heavy roller at Bradford Park Avenue.

However, these thoughts were swiftly dispatched from my mind, when the Brigadier informed me with an evil sneer to his lips:

'And I wish you to make this speech on my behalf.'

The horror!
The misery!
The despair!
Could anything be more ghastly and wretched

than the thought of making a speech at a gathering of 'cricket lovers'?

During the course of a long and undistinguished literary career I have been pestered, badgered and blackmailed on occasions too numerous to mention the length and breadth of the nation to address gatherings of so-called enthusiasts of our beloved 'summer game'.

These have come from as far apart on the compass as Land's End to Cornwall, John of Groats to Cape Wrath, the Wombwell Cricket Lovers' Society to the Jack Sokell Orphanage for Uncapped Yorkshire Occasional Seamers.

I have always refused on the grounds of incontinence and incompetence.

'No matter,' they always say. 'We don't care how bad you are at making speeches. We couldn't care less how inarticulate and drunk you are. All we want you there for is to fill in a bit of time and help us eat the disgusting food.'

I explained this to the Brigadier, but he received my explanations with a great beam of delight and understanding.

'But, of course, of course, my dear Vileness,' he said. 'The whole art of writing and delivering a cricket speech is to make it so vile, so boring, so insulting, so drab and uninteresting that they will never in a million years ask you again.'

Then he paused, rubbed his chin thoughtfully and said:

'But they always do. Oh yes, they always do.'

And thus it was that a few weeks later I presented myself at an Arab-sodden hotel in the West End of London to deliver the speech presented and written by the Brigadier in the depths of his summer-benighted study at Witney Scrotum.

I had taken the precaution of providing myself with indoor lifeboat maroons in case of emergency and wearing my numerous and distinctive campaign medals in the event of my being granted an audience with Mr Trevor Brooking – a forlorn hope, I knew, but one that would impress mightily my good friend, Mr Douglas Innersole of Essex and Wimpey Wanderers, who wisely never attends such functions and abhors all contact with former servants of West Ham United Football Club – with the profound exception, of course, of Mr Ernie Gregory of blessed and shamefully obscure memory.

The principal speaker as usual was Mr Peter Alliss who regaled his more than captive audience with intensely amusing anecdotes of a golfing nature which hardly surprised those of us who had witnessed his deft handling of his niblick during the first course, which I seemingly alone took to be soup.

Then came my turn.

I confess to having been nervous.

Never before had I been in the company of such 'celebrities'.

It had not occurred to me that gin-flavoured chocolate éclairs could be eaten by Mr Jimmy Tarbuck in the same fashion as that employed by 'the common herd' who had never been invited to take part in a Bob Hope Golf Classic or appear on the television almost live with a fat stomach and a bagful of nearly novel jokes.

Then came my turn to speak.

I tightened my Barbara Kelly patent cummerbund and my John Junkin tonsil comforter, and this is how the speech went:

'Friends,' I said. 'I realise your intense disappointment in the absence of the Brigadier at your distinguished gathering here today.

'I offer his profound apologies.

'I have to tell you that he is unable to be here with you owing to recent and painfully close contact with Mr James Anderton of the Manchester Police Force and Church of the Seventh Day Adventist Traffic Wardens.

'And so it falls to me to deliver the speech he has so carefully and painfully compiled for your delectation.'

There was a ripple of applause and the vestige of a yawn from Mr Trevor Brooking, formerly of West Ham United and an unnamed grammar school, which he is curiously proud of having attended in his youth.

I have it from impeccable sources that he got two 'O' Levels in Trapping and Passing.

And thus did I deliver the speech prepared for me by the Brigadier.

'My Lords, Your Graces, Suffragan Bishops of Congleton, Stalybridge, Macclesfield and Witton Albion, Archdeacons of Headingley, Northwich and Windsford United, Precentors of Keating New Town and Derbyshire Second XI, rural deans of Worksop and Melton Mowbray, non-selectors of MCC touring parties and Mr Jimmy Greaves, if he is fortunate enough to have an alibi.

'Why are there always so many bloody clerics at cricket functions?

'Can't you afford to buy your own food?

'Anyway, that apart, it is a great and abiding pleasure not to be here.

'I can't tell you the relief not to have to put up with the massed banks of fetid breath and the glassy-eyed battalions of unadulterated admiration and total incomprehension.

' "Who is he?" I hear you say. "Is he important in the City? Can I boast to my bank manager or crony at my local public house that I have been in the company of someone of note who has recently appeared on a chat show on the moving television?"

'No, my friends, you cannot.

'I place in my stead a total incognito, a nonentity of the profoundest quality, that Emaciated Vileness, Tinniswood, who has only been persuaded to deliver my speech in the vain hope that successful delivery of same might grant him an appearance with Miss Louise Botting on the talking wireless sponsored by the BBC.

'This speech, as are all speeches written and delivered to scum of your sort, is stunted, stilted and incompetent, and will no doubt be received by drunken raptures, owing to the simple fact that you are all without exception of a character that is both humourless and sodden by cheap port, for which you have paid inordinate amounts with your expense account plastic credit cards.

'Right then, to continue:

'I have not the slightest doubt that Tinniswood has disgraced himself by spilling copious amounts of congealed custard down the front of his hired dinner jacket, used the wrong fork for his soup, and stuck nose waste to the corner of the tablecloth.

'But what do you expect from a supporter of Lancashire County Cricket Club, an admirer of the writings of Mr Richard Brautigan and Mr Matthew Engels of *The Manchester Guardian*, a Liverpudlian and a failed writer of totally forgettable novels?

'Nonetheless, I am sure he will attempt to deliver this speech to the best of his ability, notwithstanding his bored-vowelled Cheshire accent and his catarrh-ridden Northern consonants.

'I would have asked Mr Peter Alliss to deliver the speech, but I am told he is too busy at this moment interviewing new footmen to take up duties at Buckingham Palace.

'Nevertheless, it is a great pleasure and honour to address and speak to this typical gathering of Lord's Taverners – extremely minute personalities and talents from the world of show business, directors of double glazing companies, window lock manufacturers and firms specialising in the development of clockwork home computers.

'I honour, too, the distinguished turn-out of loan sharks, property developers, inside share dealers and senior executives of Mafia-sodden Merchant banks.

'I look around me and without prejudice can say it is indeed a pleasure to be in the company of this collection of yids, darkies, Japs and half chat money lenders.

'The theme of my speech is simple.

'It is this – to honour the bicentenary of Witney Scrotum Cricket Club, the most momentous event ever to have taken place in the history of our beloved "summer game".

'Forget the winning of the Ashes in Australia

under the captaincy of Bombardier Mike Gatting. Forget the desecration of Bramall Lane. Forget the beatification of Mr Raymond Illingworth and the ritual cleaning of Mr Barry Wood. Forget, even, the spectacular coronation of Mr. E. R. "Elizabeth Regina" Dexter at St Paul's and the wedding in Westminster Abbey of Prince Andrew to the lady who looks so remarkably like Mr Eddie Hemmings.

'No, it is Witney Scrotum that dominates all our thoughts.

'Two hundred years!

'Is it really longer than a television quiz show hosted by Mr Leslie Crowther?

'Is it indeed almost as long as the series of repeats of *The Two Ronnies?*

'Yet here we are still flourishing in the prime of our existence: Miss Roebuck from the dog biscuit shop still busily cutting the crusts off the Marmite sandwiches for tea; Gooch, the village blacksmith, still stumping out to open the innings in his armour-plated Wellingtons and cast-iron moustache warmer, Prodger the poacher still exposing himself assiduously at the long-on boundary.

'Let us think back over those years, those two momentous centuries when the welfare and prosperity of our nation has been inextricably linked with the affairs of Witney Scrotum.

'1787 – the year of our establishment.

'Two years before the sacking of the Bastille. Two years before the sacking of Brian Close from Yorkshire County Cricket Club.

'And what mighty events we have witnessed during the span of those years.

'The invention, the triumph and the demise of the electric tram car.

'The rejection of bicycle clips by vast sections of the civilised world.

'The disappearance of the pyjama cord and the dominance of one-day cricket played in fancy dress.

'We have witnessed wars and revolutions of the basest and most calamitous of natures.

'We think of the Napoleonic Wars, the two Boer Wars, the Great Depression, the revolutions of '48 which swept through Europe like a raging fire and subsequently brought to prominence the bowling of Mr Tom Cartwright and the batting of Mr Trevor Bailey.

'Yet during all these calamities and deprivations we have consoled ourselves with one thing – the purity, the hope, the triumph, the ultimate truth of the game of cricket.

'Come on, you bastards, stop nodding off. Pour yourself another glass of over-expensive and disgusting wine.

'Pay attention, you scum.

'I'm talking about this – even in the most hopeless and darkest days of drought, famine, pestilence, natural disasters and cricket reports of Mr Tony Lewis we have consoled ourselves that ultimately there would appear on the scene like a bright, shining, translucent light Lord Henry Blofeld and his legions of typewriter wallahs and personal manufacturers of bespoke Subba Row black silk trousers.

'And this is the other theme of my speech – if you drunken scum can keep awake.

'However dark the days of the present and the

government's plans to privatise the manufacture of oven gloves and typewriter ribbons, however dastardly the days of the future with the prospect of the Ink Monitor at Number Ten appearing in perpetuity on the *Jimmy Young Show*, we know that one day there will always be in this great nation of ours a person who will "rise to the occasion" and ensure that Britannia will rule the waves and we will once again knock the living daylights out of dagos, darkies and disgusting foreigners of every creed and kin, and life as we know it will once again reign supreme in the shape of committee members of Yorkshire County Cricket Club.

'And here, gentlemen, I pay my respects, and the respects of one and all at Witney Scrotum, to the long and honourable history of the Lord's Taverners.

'Am I rambling?

'Yes I am.

'Everyone rambles in a cricket speech.

'It's the only way to cope.

'It's the only way to . . .

'My friends, the one consolation I have in all the vicissitudes which afflict me in this modern way of life of ours is the assurance that it is still possible, despite pop videos on the moving television and the absence of gritting lorries in winter . . . is that it is still possible to take a cruise with the Lord's Taverners on HMS *Canberra*.

'How moving. How reassuring.

'Consider carefully the case of Rear Admiral Tony Swainson, commander-in-chief of the Lord's Taverners.

'This noble, selfless man has taken part, despite

all the rigours and hardships, in every Taverners' voyage from Magellan's discovery of Tierra del Fuego to the opening up of trading relations with Mr Vivian Richards and the Windward Island.

'Not only has he driven the ships on each expedition, but he has also been selfless in the filling in of old ladies' bingo cards, the entertainment of coach parties from Halifax and Barrow-in-Furness and the guiding of Mr Willie Rushton to the forrard bar – which he describes so aptly and nautically as "the watering hole at the pointed end of the boat".

'Thus is the work of the Lord's Taverners and all its members, and I salute it unreservedly.

'Gentlemen, for the past two hours we have suffered deprivations of the most unimaginable sort.

'We have stood side-by-side in the gents' urinals glancing furtively at each other's equipment of a cricketing nature.

'We have swapped yarns of dire days spent in pantomime in Milton Keynes and selling shopping piazzas to the townsfolk of Melton Mowbray.

'And we have been united by one thing and one thing alone – cricket.

'Let us, to use the words of the sublime Ink Monitor at Number Ten, when she rescued her son from the great Falkland Island motor rally, "Rejoice, gentlemen, rejoice."

'Rejoice, my friends, to two thousand years of the existence of the Lord's Taverners.

'Two thousand years of attending luncheons and dinners served up so shamelessly by the eating establishments so carelessly chosen by your committee.

'Two thousand years of forcing down Consommé à la Crapp, Veal Cutlets Dujon and Appleyard Strudel with cricket bag sauce.

'Ah, I see I strike a chord.

'I see you looking at your neighbours.

'I see you thinking to yourselves – is he famous for being famous, did he possibly once go in fifth wicket down for Worcestershire, does he know the intimate secrets of the life of Mr Bill Alley and Mr Colin Dredge?

'Is it possible that one day I myself might achieve the ultimate accolade of being selected to take a cruise with the Taverners and find myself seated next to Mr Bill Tidy?

'Is it conceivable that I might actually have the chance of speaking in person to the great and noble Mr Pete Murray, whose devotion to the cause of cruising is a byword in the annals of the P&O Steamship Company?

'Such hopes, I know, are beyond the reaches of mortal man.

'But console yourselves with this thought, my friends.

'You are in the company of like minds – drunks, louts and congenital layabouts.

'You have dined together in easy approbation.

'You might be worrying – oh God, I've got to give a signed ten-pound note for the raffle in aid of the Jimmy Tarbuck caddy cart for underprivileged stand-up comedians. Don't.

'Think thus:

'You are here to give thanks to cricket.

'And, when you arrive home, drunk, legless and totally incapacitated, and are confronted by lady

wives, mistresses or live-in spinster retired Royal
Navy stokers, all you have to say are those noble
ringing words, which have so distinguished our
beloved "summer game" and raised it to a peak of
excellence far beyond the pathetic endeavours of
any other game:

  ' "Sorry, darling, but I had to have an extra drink
with Denis Compton." '

9

The Great Day

THE GREAT DAY ARRIVED.

The Australians were to play a one-day Test against Witney Scrotum.

All preparations had been made for their visit.

Every woman of child-bearing age had been dispatched to the Outer Hebrides.

The county yeomanry, the Duke of Marlar's Own Gripers and Fencibles, had been on red alert.

For three days Miss Roebuck from the dog biscuit shop had been busy mucking out Farmer Emburey's stables to provide overnight accommodation for the visitors from 'Down Under'.

The Cricket Bag Repository had donated sacking and sawdust for their bedding, and the fire brigade had installed a static tank in the unlikely event of their wishing to wash themselves.

The entertainments committee had arranged a full

day's programme of activities, including an exhibition of traditional nude limbo dancing by old Grannie Swanton and a display of mass wife-swapping by the Witney Scrotum train spotters' club.

Unfortunately I myself could not be present.

It was the day of the parrot's annual MOT test.

It was, therefore, with extreme excitement and anticipation that I visited Witney Scrotum a month later to enquire from the Brigadier what had happened.

He looked at me silently for a moment, and then he said:

'It rained.

'It rained and it rained and it rained.

'And I knew it would.'

There was a long, slow silence.

'Is that all?' I ventured.

'No,' said the Brigadier.

There was another pause.

The clock ticked.

The clock tocked.

'Well?' I said.

The Brigadier sucked hard at his slucking pipe and presently he said:

'The Australians didn't turn up.

'The buggers didn't turn up.

'I knew they wouldn't.'

After a while we repaired for lunchtime snorters with the Commodore in his summer house.

Under the circumstances it seemed the only sensible thing to do.

We got drunk and made three nuisance calls to dear old Bruce Woodcock of *The Times*.

It cheered us up enormously.

Stop Press

A FRENZIED HAMMERING at my front door.

Screech of parrot. Baying of dog. Faint whimpers from sleep-bound wife.

I lurched stiff-limbed downstairs, my knee joints creaking, my slippers snarling and snapping at the cord of my dressing-gown.

The hammering continued. Fists beating on complaining timber. Louder and louder grew the noise. It shook and swayed the current week's delivery of free newspapers which stood in a chest-high pile by the umbrella stand. It threatened to dislodge the Neighbourhood Watch sticker attached to the leaded lights.

Dear God, if that came off, we were really in deep trouble, for it was the only thing holding the front door together.

In a panic I dragged back the Nourse and Rowan

148

patent burglar-proof bolts, unhooked the Rhodes and Kilner novelty security chain, released the Ring and Toshack reversible ratchet anti-Jehovah's Witness lock and flung open the front door.

Facing me was the Brigadier.

His face was flushed scarlet. His chest was heaving. There were beads of perspiration standing out on his plus fours.

'Whatho, Vileness,' he said, entered the hallway and instantly performed an eighteen-foot glissade on his backside after stepping on seven assorted and unopened plastic-coated begging letters and brochures from American Express.

He picked himself up with an oath, dusted down his spats and led me into my study.

He slammed the door firmly behind us and looked round the room furtively.

'Is it sound-proof?' he whispered.

'I think so,' I said. 'The wife never seems to hear when I'm bathing the tortoise.'

'Good, good,' he said, and he commenced to prowl round the room, sniffing at the wallpaper and turning up the corners of rugs, crawling on hands and knees beneath my indoor bike shed and searching the tops of my pelmets with his inflatable torch.

'What on earth are you doing?' I said.

'Making sure the room isn't bugged,' he said.

'It isn't,' I said. 'It's at least two years since my mother-in-law was here.'

'Good,' he said. 'Good.'

He advanced on my armchair, swept it clear of its mounds of half-fermenting back copies of *The Cricketer* and the *Beano* annuals I was currently translating into Swedish and seated himself with a grunt and a groan.

He smiled.

He plunged his hands deep into the depths of his hand-knitted Barbour coat and produced from the poacher's pocket a large brown manilla envelope.

He handed it to me with a broad grin.

'Well, Vileness,' he said. 'What do you think?'

I examined the envelope. It was full to bursting point. On its back was an aged stain I took to be either a smear of congealed Cooper's chunky marmalade or a sample of Mr David Gower's personal stick deodorant.

On the front was printed in large letters:

'MCC – OFFICIAL DOCUMENTS – MOST CONFIDENTIAL AND SECRET.'

'Good God,' I said. 'Where did you get this from?'

'I found it on the train,' said the Brigadier. 'Some careless swine obviously dropped it from his brief-case. Talk about hot property, eh, Vileness? Talk about a national scandal. Do you think it will bring the government down? Do you think it will force Alec Bedser to change his suit?'

I shrugged my shoulders.

'Well, open the bloody thing then, blast you,' said the Brigadier. 'Open it and look inside.'

I opened the envelope and extracted the contents. The briefest of cursory glances was enough to make me gasp with astonishment.

The Brigadier chuckled with delight and slapped his thighs with the blunt end of his stumper's mallet.

'Well?' he said. 'What do you think? Is it the end

of the world as we know it? Does it spell the demise of western civilisation and the Welsh rarebit?'

I was speechless.

There in front of me was a wad of notes and manuscripts headed:

'The New Official Two Hundred Years History of Lord's and MCC as written by Mr Tony Lewis, writer, broadcaster, famous cricketer and thoroughly good egg.'

For a moment I felt like a theatrical archivist might feel discovering an unknown Shakespeare folio or an unrecorded bound volume of the collected works of Mr Ray Cooney.

I felt like an archaeologist entering for the first time the tomb of Tutankhamen in the inner depths of the Yorkshire dressing-room.

I felt like Amundsen when he reached the South Pole just short of a length at the Stretford End, Old Trafford.

The Brigadier chuckled again.

'I told you they were hatching up something at Lord's,' he said. 'Two hundred years of history my foot! They're just trying to cash in on our celebrations at Witney Scrotum. They're trying to outdo us. Well, Vileness, we've caught them with their trousers down, eh?'

I nodded absent-mindedly.

In truth that aspect of the matter did not concern me greatly. What fascinated and excited and thrilled me was the fact that I had in my possession the original notes and manuscripts of one of the towering giants not only of cricket writing, but of the whole caucus of English literature itself, Mr

Tony Lewis – and it was written in real, joined-up writing.

'Go on then,' said the Brigadier. 'You might as well read it. No one else will unless they sell it off at half price in the Masochists' Book Club.'

How my heart soared as I read those first noble words:

'The bicentenary of the MCC starts two hundred years ago.

'What a long time ago isn't it?

'It certainly makes you think.'

And in the margin alongside was written in inedible pencil:

'What *does* it make you think about? I must ask Tim Heald. He'll be bound to think of something I can use.'

As I read on I was staggered by Mr Lewis's erudition and the breadth and originality of his research.

I confess I was totally ignorant of the fact that the First World War had been fought from 1913 to 1919.

I had not the faintest idea that Mr Richie Benaud was a member of the Swiss Royal Family.

I was astounded by the author's revelations that the scorecard printing presses at headquarters were build out of Leggo by Mr Geoffrey Moorhouse – 'Whose books I must dip into one day,' wrote Mr Lewis.

And I was, of course, enchanted by the magic and typical Celtic lilt of his prose.

I quote:

'Lord's is a very famous cricket ground.

'It is very big, too.

'Lots of very famous cricketers have played there.

'That's why it's such a nice place to go to watch cricket at, if, of course, that is your predilection and you like cricket as well.'

For scholars of the 'summer game', of course, it was the legion of margin notes which provided the most stimulation and intellectual satisfaction.

I quote from a few:

'Is Denis Compton a right-handed bat or a left-handed bat? I must check with Jonners, who seems to know about such things.'

'How do you spell Ranjitwhatshisname? I must look it up in my Roget's Thesor . . . Thessir . . . how do you spell Thesaurus?'

'I must look up Sir Pelham Warner's telephone number.'

'Which is the Pavilion End and which is the Nursery End? I'll drop a line to John Arlott, who will probably have some ideas on the subject and might send me a free bottle of vintage claret. Is that red wine or is it white? I must check with Jonners, who seems to know about such things.'

'Why do they call it Lord's? I must find out. It might be jolly interesting.'

'I must remember to comb my teeth when I go on *Start the Week* to publicise the book.'

'When the captains toss a coin to see who's won the toss, how do they know which side is heads and which side is tails? I'll give Bill Frindall a bell. It's bound to be in one of his reference books if he's not too busy talking to himself on his answering machine.'

'Why not do a chapter about famous matches at Lord's? There must have been some. I bet Jonners knows. I'll go round to see him and he might give

me a free dinner. Which spoon do you use to eat
your peas with?'

But then came the real 'hot stuff'.

The last sheet of notes was headed:

'The scandal at Lord's, winter 1986/87.'

I pass the notes on to you as they stand and
without comment:

'Parties in the Long Room . . . Cynthia Payne . . .
old men in nothing but MCC spats . . . funny place
for a jock strap . . . I wonder who this bloke Fellatio
is? He's either a Sri Lankan opening bat or he plays
inside right for Argentina . . . subtle changes to no
ball rules . . . lady dressed in nothing but cricket
sweater. Must find out which county it was . . .
crikey, they don't do things like that in Neath – not
in so many words, anyway . . . I never used linseed
oil for that . . . so that's why he could never get a
full length with his top spinner.'

I read on into the night.

I finished the documents exhausted both phys-
ically and emotionally.

I looked up.

The Brigadier was sound asleep in my armchair,
his pipe resting in his lap, the front of his cardigan
covered in a complex archipelago of tobacco burns.

What should I do with the manuscript?

Send it to MI5?

Leak it to Chapman Pincher?

Sell it to the *Observer?*

No.

No, I could not bring our beloved 'summer game'
into such disrepute.

There was only one thing to do.

I tossed the envelope and its contents on to the fire.

And as I watched them smoulder damply and then burst into a brief flicker of red and yellow flamelets and finally subside into a mound of sullen ash, I felt that the world was indeed a far, far better place for my actions.

A Selection of Arrow Bestsellers

☐ The Lilac Bus	Maeve Binchy	£2.50
☐ 500 Mile Walkies	Mark Wallington	£2.50
☐ Staying Off the Beaten Track	Elizabeth Gundrey	£5.95
☐ A Better World Than This	Marie Joseph	£2.95
☐ No Enemy But Time	Evelyn Anthony	£2.95
☐ Rates of Exchange	Malcolm Bradbury	£3.50
☐ Colours Aloft	Alexander Kent	£2.95
☐ Speaker for the Dead	Orson Scott Card	£2.95
☐ Eon	Greg Bear	£4.95
☐ Talking to Strange Men	Ruth Rendell	£5.95
☐ Heartstones	Ruth Rendell	£2.50
☐ Rosemary Conley's Hip and Thigh Diet	Rosemary Conley	£2.50
☐ Communion	Whitley Strieber	£3.50
☐ The Ladies of Missalonghi	Colleen McCullough	£2.50
☐ Erin's Child	Sheelagh Kelly	£3.99
☐ Sarum	Edward Rutherfurd	£4.50

Prices and other details are liable to change

ARROW BOOKS, BOOKSERVICE BY POST, PO BOX 29, DOUGLAS, ISLE OF MAN, BRITISH ISLES

NAME...

ADDRESS..

....

....

Please enclose a cheque or postal order made out to Arrow Books Ltd. for the amount due and allow the following for postage and packing.

U.K. CUSTOMERS: Please allow 22p per book to a maximum of £3.00.

B.F.P.O. & EIRE: Please allow 22p per book to a maximum of £3.00

OVERSEAS CUSTOMERS: Please allow 22p per book.

Whilst every effort is made to keep prices low it is sometimes necessary to increase cover prices at short notice. Arrow Books reserve the right to show new retail prices on covers which may differ from those previously advertised in the text or elsewhere.

Bestselling SF/Horror

☐ The Labyrinth	Robert Faulcon	£2.50
☐ Night Train	Thomas F. Monteleone	£2.50
☐ Malleus Maleficarum	Montague Summers	£4.50
☐ The Devil Rides Out	Dennis Wheatley	£2.50
☐ The Shadow of the Torturer	Gene Wolfe	£2.95
☐ Contact	Carl Sagan	£3.50
☐ Cobra Strike (Venture SF 17)	Timothy Zahn	£2.95
☐ Night Visions	Campbell, Barker, Tuttle	£2.95
☐ Bones of the Moon	Jonathan Carroll	£2.50
☐ The Island	Guy N. Smith	£2.50
☐ The Hungry Moon	Ramsey Campbell	£2.95
☐ Pin	Andrew Neiderman	£1.50

Prices and other details are liable to change

ARROW BOOKS, BOOKSERVICE BY POST, PO BOX 29, DOUGLAS, ISLE OF MAN, BRITISH ISLES

NAME. . . . .

ADDRESS. . . . .

. . . .

. . . .

Please enclose a cheque or postal order made out to Arrow Books Ltd. for the amount due and allow the following for postage and packing.

U.K. CUSTOMERS: Please allow 22p per book to a maximum of £3.00.

B.F.P.O. & EIRE: Please allow 22p per book to a maximum of £3.00

OVERSEAS CUSTOMERS: Please allow 22p per book.

Whilst every effort is made to keep prices low it is sometimes necessary to increase cover prices at short notice. Arrow Books reserve the right to show new retail prices on covers which may differ from those previously advertised in the text or elsewhere.

Bestselling Thriller/Suspense

☐ Hell is Always Today	Jack Higgins	£2.50
☐ Brought in Dead	Harry Patterson	£1.99
☐ Russian Spring	Dennis Jones	£2.50
☐ Fletch	Gregory Mcdonald	£1.95
☐ Black Ice	Colin Dunne	£2.50
☐ Blind Run	Brian Freemantle	£2.50
☐ The Proteus Operation	James P. Hogan	£3.50
☐ Miami One Way	Mike Winters	£2.50
☐ Skydancer	Geoffrey Archer	£2.50
☐ Hour of the Lily	John Kruse	£3.50
☐ The Tunnel	Stanley Johnson	£2.50
☐ The Albatross Run	Douglas Scott	£2.50
☐ Dragonfire	Andrew Kaplan	£2.99

Prices and other details are liable to change

ARROW BOOKS, BOOKSERVICE BY POST, PO BOX 29, DOUGLAS, ISLE OF MAN, BRITISH ISLES

NAME...

ADDRESS..

....

....

Please enclose a cheque or postal order made out to Arrow Books Ltd. for the amount due and allow the following for postage and packing.

U.K. CUSTOMERS: Please allow 22p per book to a maximum of £3.00.

B.F.P.O. & EIRE: Please allow 22p per book to a maximum of £3.00

OVERSEAS CUSTOMERS: Please allow 22p per book.

Whilst every effort is made to keep prices low it is sometimes necessary to increase cover prices at short notice. Arrow Books reserve the right to show new retail prices on covers which may differ from those previously advertised in the text or elsewhere.

Bestselling Humour

☐ Carrott Roots	Jasper Carrott	£3.50
☐ The Art of Course Office Life	Michael Green	£1.95
☐ Rambling On	Mike Harding	£2.50
☐ Sex Tips for Girls	Cynthia Heimel	£2.95
☐ Sex Tips for Boys	William Davis	£2.95
☐ Tales from a Long Room	Peter Tinniswood	£2.75
☐ Tales from Whitney Scrotum	Peter Tinniswood	£2.50
☐ Why Come to Slaka?	Malcolm Bradbury	£2.95
☐ Football is a Funny Game	Ian St. John & Jimmy Greaves	£3.95
☐ The Bedside Book of Sex	Rolf White	£2.95
☐ Palace	Neil Mackwood & Bryan Rostron	£2.50
☐ Tim Brooke-Taylor's Cricket Box	Tim Brooke-Taylor	£4.50

Prices and other details are liable to change

ARROW BOOKS, BOOKSERVICE BY POST, PO BOX 29, DOUGLAS, ISLE OF MAN, BRITISH ISLES

NAME...

ADDRESS...

....

....

Please enclose a cheque or postal order made out to Arrow Books Ltd. for the amount due and allow the following for postage and packing.

U.K. CUSTOMERS: Please allow 22p per book to a maximum of £3.00.

B.F.P.O. & EIRE: Please allow 22p per book to a maximum of £3.00 .

OVERSEAS CUSTOMERS: Please allow 22p per book.

Whilst every effort is made to keep prices low it is sometimes necessary to increase cover prices at short notice. Arrow Books reserve the right to show new retail prices on covers which may differ from those previously advertised in the text or elsewhere.